'You know what you do to me, don't you?'

Chelsea took a deep breath, her body pulsing. She felt his strong hands on the curve of her shoulders, and her breath trembled at the gentle touch of his lips against her forehead. The faint, erotic scent of him beneath the subtlety of his cologne was threatening to drive her wild. Why did she have to feel like this—and about him, of all people?

'No, don't...' She averted her face to avoid the arousing tenderness of his mouth. 'There's too much between us, Paolo.'

His lips caressed her hairline, whispered into the tangled, silken gold. 'Our mutual chemistries tell us that we were meant to be. You can't pretend it isn't true, can you?'

Elizabeth Power was born in Bristol, where she lives with her husband in a three-hundred-year-old cottage. A keen reader, as a teenager she had already made up her mind to be a novelist, although it wasn't until around thirty that she took up writing seriously. She is an animal lover with a strong leaning towards vegetarianism, and her interests include organic vegetable gardening, regular exercise, listening to music, fashion and ministering to the demands of her adopted, generously proportioned cat!

Recent titles by the same author:

TERMS OF POSSESSION

JILTED BRIDE

BY
ELIZABETH POWER

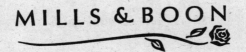

MILLS & BOON

MILLS & BOON and the Rose Device
are trademarks of the publisher.
Harlequin Mills & Boon Limited,
Eton House, 18-24 Paradise Road, Richmond, Surrey TW9 1SR

© Elizabeth Power 1996

ISBN 0 263 79812 7

Set in Times Roman 9½ on 10½ pt.
01-9611-66990 C1

Made and printed in Great Britain

CHAPTER ONE

WHERE the hell *was* he?

From behind a screen of ivory lace, Chelsea could see everyone already seated in the church, and from where she was standing, just outside the main door, could sense the beginnings of restless speculation. Was there going to be a wedding—without a groom?

'He was up, bright and breezy, when I popped round first thing,' Murray, tall and blond and dashing in his grey morning suit, supplied to try and ease her agitation over the absence of his younger brother. 'You know Julian. He'd already had his game of squash, showered, and was spouting investment tips down the phone to someone even before seven this morning—so he's got no excuse for being late.'

Only he was. Over half an hour late, Chelsea thought, nibbling her lower lip, finding little comfort in the best man's futile attempts to appear unconcerned, because she knew he had to be thinking exactly what she was. That even if Julian Rendell was a committed workaholic, a wizard in financial affairs with some pretty impressive clients, in one thing he was always, sometimes maddeningly, predictable—he was never late.

'Perhaps it's dawned upon him what a crazy thing he's doing and he's decided to opt out while he's still got the chance.'

The cool summer breeze gently lifted Chelsea's veil and she shuddered, though more at her father's coldly cynical remark than anything else. And quick as a dart, so that she braced herself for its impact, came her mother's voice. 'How can you say that? This is your daughter's big day and you have to try and ruin it by coming out with a thing like that. Can't you understand how nervous she must be feeling

5

anyway—giving up her independence? Knowing after today her life won't be her own any more?'

It was something that Chelsea had expected, this familiar bickering between her parents. It was the reason why she had moved into her own flat four years ago—just after her eighteenth birthday; one of the reasons she was so determined to have a happy marriage of her own. She had hoped, though, that her parents' two-year separation might have tempered their eternal need to argue with one another, but now she exhaled a small, involuntary sigh. She should have known better.

'Then why the dickens does she want to do it? Apart from which, I can only see marriage for Julian as a bonus on the social ladder he's clearly set his sights on climbing.' Her father droned on, only aggravating the worries that were beginning to surface in Chelsea, every word a sword to fight his own disillusionment with the marital bond.

'For heaven's sake! This isn't helping things at all!' With that huskily breathed declaration Chelsea was lifting her veil, turning it back, only to evoke an anxious response from her mother.

'You shouldn't do that, dear. It's bad luck.'

Bad luck? There was raw tension in the model-fine features that Chelsea had revealed, anxiety in the subtly shadowed brown eyes.

'How much worse can it get? He'd already left when Murray rang him twenty minutes ago!' Sunlight streaked the blonde, shoulder-length bobbed hair as she glanced towards the car from where the best man had made the call. 'That means he should be here by now. Something must have happened to him. An accident...!'

She was getting overwrought, which wasn't like her at all. Usually she took things in her stride. Perhaps it was this waiting around, the whole spectacle of the day which was nothing like the quiet ceremony that she would have preferred, but she had wanted to please Julian and, even more, her parents, hoping that the showy celebration her mother at least had requested for her only daughter—the

Cinderella dress, the assembly of forgotten relatives—might revive certain memories, the promises that each had made— so long ago—to the other. Or perhaps it was because of what her mother had just said about bad luck...

'Stop worrying.' Susan, her chief bridesmaid, vivaciously dark in lilac satin, laid a reassuring hand on her arm. 'He might be the catch of the century, but *he's* not doing so badly either. If he had the slightest misgivings about today...' her soft laughter and her glance towards Rupert Adamson ridiculed the very concept '...he'd be a fool, and both you and I know he's certainly not that.'

No, he wasn't, Chelsea reflected, thinking of Julian's calculating shrewdness in business, and smiling a silent thank-you to her friend for her loyalty and support. She wondered what everyone would think if they knew it was her own misgivings that were troubling her. Because, unintentionally, her parents' tactless remarks had given rise to those unaccountable doubts—those fears which, for weeks now, had been quietly niggling in the background, forcing her to question her feelings, ask herself over and over, Was she really doing the right thing?

Seven years older than she was, Julian had been her first and only boyfriend, and when they had announced their engagement last year it had made her very happy to realise that they were doing exactly what both their families had always expected of them—even Neil: Neil, whom she needed to talk to today, whose reassurance she would desperately have loved. But the cousin on whom she doted had declined their wedding invitation, his letter from Canada wishing them well but informing them that he was too busy to get away.

Maybe he was, she thought, although between the lines of that letter she had read more in his refusal than just the pressure of his job and knew it was because of Julian. Ever since he had got mixed up with *that man*...

'Of course he'll be here. My son wouldn't be the success he is today if he couldn't be relied upon, Chelsea.' Short and blonde and striking in her royal blue outfit, Muriel

Rendell looked as smug as ever to be crooning over her younger son's achievements.

'Well, he isn't being very reliable now, is he?' came Rupert Adamson's irate observation.

A sturdily built Yorkshireman, he was pulling uncomfortably at his stiff, starched collar. Beyond the church doors, the restless shuffling had increased.

'The vicar says he's got another wedding in twenty minutes. Oh, my poor lamb! You're going to have to face the fact—he isn't coming.'

Numbed, disbelieving, Chelsea stared at her mother, who had just emerged from inside. Fair and still youthful, yet well into her forties, her mother, Chelsea knew, judged all men by her own disenchantment.

'He wouldn't just not turn up. Something must have happened!' A dark fear filled Chelsea's eyes as she looked from one to the other of her parents. 'He could be lying there in his flat—collapsed or something. That's why he didn't answer when Murray rang him! He's got a phone in the car. If he'd broken down or something he'd have let us know by now. I've got to go to him!' She turned entreatingly to the slim, stunned figure of her mother, begging, 'Mum, let me have your keys. He might be back there wounded, and I'm waiting here like some—'

'Chelsea!' About to dart away, she turned sharply towards Murray, who was hurrying towards them from the direction of the vicarage. She hadn't even realised he'd gone anywhere. 'I've just had a message from the vicar's wife! I'm afraid Julian won't be coming.' The best man's words sounded unreal, distant in her ears. 'I don't know how to tell you this...'

'He's had an accident!' The truth of what she had feared seemed to weaken every bone in her body, and with trembling fingers she pulled back the impeding lace blowing across her face. 'He's crashed the car!'

'No, it's nothing like that.' The blue eyes, so much like Julian's, were sympathetic as they gazed down on her fine features, which appeared bloodless against the pale gold of her hair. 'He ... he's had to fly to Milan ...'

'*Milan*!' Her exclamation drowned the simultaneous gasps from the small family gathering and the three brides-maids, who were waiting futilely now in their lilac finery; her brown eyes searched for a sign from Julian's brother that this was some ridiculous practical joke.

But Murray, like Julian, was too serious-minded for practical jokes. Hectically, she tried to marshal her thoughts, to think through the confusion, bewilderment and hurt anger that was suddenly bubbling through her.

'It's to do with *him*, isn't it?' She tossed up at Murray accusingly. 'With Rossetti.'

Paolo Rossetti. Perfumer. Couturier. And heaven knew what else the man was king of besides the world-famous House of Rossetti! Rossetti. The name on every fashion-conscious woman's lips worldwide—and constantly on Julian's. The man who through a mutual acquaintance had discovered Julian's brilliance and appointed him as one of his UK advisors. Paolo Rossetti. The man who had ruined her cousin.

'Julian thinks the man owns his entire life!' Her voice cracking, she choked back the sob in her throat. 'How could he let anything be more important to him than our wedding?'

Hurting, hopelessly she glanced around, catching the re-signed look on her prospective mother-in-law's face, the unconcealed annoyance on her father's.

'I don't know.' Murray was playing the go-between, and looked uneasy doing it. 'He said he left a message for you on your father's answering machine. Said he knows you'll understand.'

'*Understand*?' Bitter tears scalded her eyes. How could he do it—leave her here like this ...?

Sightlessly she glanced down at the scentless bouquet of pale orchids that she was clutching against the paler ivory of her bodice. He'd wanted her draped head to foot in white, to have this big wedding with all the trimmings. So how could he desert her—abandon her like this at the whim of a man whom he knew she despised, and with solid foundation?

'What am I supposed to understand?' She looked up at Murray, battling against her tears. 'That Paolo Rossetti's more important to him than me?'

'Than *I,* dear,' Muriel Rendell corrected her, with that penchant for precision that she had passed on to both her sons and which at times, like now, Chelsea found infuriating. 'If Julian has had to go to Milan then he will have had a very good reason. After all, by putting his trust in Julian's abilities, Mr Rossetti's made it possible for you both to look forward to a very comfortable future.' Her voice had increased considerably in volume, as it always did when she was happily dropping names. 'I think most couples would give their eye-teeth to have an opportunity like that.'

Meaning that she should be tolerant about being left standing at the church! Chelsea interpreted, too unhappy and unhinged by the thought of what to say to everyone inside to respond. One or two people were already peering out, having heard the commotion going on in the porch.

'I don't care what opportunities he thinks he's got, Muriel. There isn't one single thing that couldn't have waited until after they were wed.' Through her racing emotions Chelsea heard her father loyally defending her, felt his stabilising arm around her shoulders. 'Come on, lass. I think I'd better take you home.'

'And what about all those in there?' Jennifer Adamson gave a meaningful toss of her head towards the pews of impatient guests. 'What are we going to tell *them*?'

'Most of them are your relatives—*you* think of something.'

Chelsea barely heard her parents' thoughtless wrangling, or her mother's, 'Don't let her drive in that state,' as she wrenched off her veil and headdress and thrust them, with her bouquet, at the surprised Susan. The following, 'You drive her, but bring my car straight back!' sent her flying down the church path, away from their petty squabbling and the pain of her own humiliation, as if her feet had wings.

Guests already arriving for the next wedding stared at her as she deliberately abandoned the shining silver limousine that had brought her for her mother's little red two-door saloon.

If Julian wanted a show, then she'd give him one! she decided as she landed with a rather ungainly bump on the back seat and tugged the cumbersome dress in after her. If he preferred to be with Paolo Rossetti then let him have him!

'Are you all right, love?' Rupert asked her when they were out on the open road, speeding away.

She wasn't, but she nodded, seeing his concerned eyes in the rear-view mirror. He hated weddings. Probably all he wanted to do was to get home—home to his pigeons.

'I don't know what's wrong with Muriel these days,' he went on, as though he needed to excuse his old friend's wife's behaviour. 'She's become totally insensitive since she lost Oliver.'

But so are you. *You and Mum*! she wanted to scream, but she didn't, only saying in response to his remark about Julian's widowed mother, 'I think she's just easily impressed.'

'By this Rossetti?' Her father's jaw hardened as he was forced to bring the car to a near standstill in the busy London traffic. 'For heaven's sake, the man *is* human! What's wrong with Julian? I'm sure if he'd been firmer— explained that he was getting married—the man would have been prepared to have given him some leeway.'

'Like he did with Neil?' The comment escaped her, poignant and festering, and she saw those troubled paternal eyes briefly in the rear-view mirror again before they turned away.

'Aye, well . . .'

He didn't want to talk about it. Neither of her parents did if ever she broached the subject, and right then Neil's problems were the last thing on her mind.

Julian had jilted her—that was all her tormented brain could think about. And all because of that Italian—the man she hated. Whom she had never met—never wanted to. And yet over whom they had had countless arguments.

'Rossetti's worth a fortune to my firm,' Julian had stressed once when she had objected to having their married life as good as financed by the man who had caused such devastating grief to her cousin. 'It would be unfair to my partners to turn away all the security his investments are going to bring to this company—as well as ludicrous! Look at it this way,' he'd gone on in more mollifying tones, to try to appease her, 'it's not as though you personally will ever have anything to do with him. And you can look on every penny we earn from Rossetti as payment of the debt you feel he owes Neil.'

Only it wasn't, Chelsea reflected with biting resentment as her father brought the car through the smart suburb and drew up outside the detached house that had once been the family home. No amount of money could compensate for the brutal way that that Italian had treated her cousin, only Julian couldn't see it that way.

The message he'd left on the answering machine did little to explain why he had felt justified in leaving her as he had, filling her with an upsurge of angry emotion as she listened to his voice on the tape.

'There's been a terrible misunderstanding with Rossetti, Chelsea, and he wants me there immediately. He's sent his private jet—so I have to go. I'm sorry, but there really isn't any other choice. I'll be in touch as soon as I can.' And that was all. No explanation. No justification. Nothing.

Fighting back bitter sobs, she was tearing off the ridiculous confection of a dress before she had even reached her room, the unaccustomed upheaval of her old bedroom—strewn with boxes, tissue-paper and the congratulatory telegrams that had arrived in the post that morning—cutting into her already wounded pride.

Through the initial pain and humiliation, however, other feelings had started to surface that she was too shocked by to admit to—feelings that made her question whether she shouldn't be grateful for this chance to examine thoroughly the way she felt about Julian. She pulled on a blue satin robe and flopped down onto the dressing-table stool.

Rupert Adamson knocked and came in with a cup of tea. It was her father's remedy for everything, she remembered, and after she had drunk it she did feel more in control.

'What are you going to do?' she heard him say softly, no doubt recognising the familiar squaring of her shoulders, the battle-poised lifting of her chin.

'Do?' Purposefully she stared at her pale reflection in the mirror, as though challenging it to oppose her, because Julian Rendell wasn't going to get away with this! If he thought she was going to play second fiddle to a man like Paolo Rossetti he had another think coming! Besides, there had been a weird note in his voice on that recorded message that had made him sound...different somehow. And, glancing up at the man in the mirror who looked more like his usual self now that he had discarded the formal jacket and tie and unbuttoned his shirt, she said determinedly, 'I'm going to Milan.'

Her stomach was fluttering nervously as the taxi swerved to avoid one of the endless number of cyclists that they had met on the way from the airport and drew up outside the prestigious, modern headquarters of Rossetti.

'You want it?' The driver gestured flamboyantly towards the imposing building with that world-famous signature emblazoned across the front. 'It is here.'

Thanking him, Chelsea paid the fare, her stomach muscles contracting into a tight knot, despite her air of outward calm, as she made her way inside to the impersonal marbled semicircle of the reception desk.

'*Buongiorno.*' An elegant receptionist greeted her in Italian as Chelsea's eyes registered the marble steps on her left leading to some lifts.

'Do—do you speak English?'

'*Sì.*' In thickly accented English, efficiently the woman asked how she could help.

'I wish to see Mr Rossetti,' Chelsea answered with an unconscious lift of her chin, because she hadn't failed to notice that bronze bust of the great man standing on a marble plinth in the centre of the foyer with its engraved brass plaque beneath it. A man in his late fifties, she assessed, taking in the high forehead, the straight nose and hard mouth; a man still attractive enough to take his pick of young women obviously smitten by his wealth and power. As the girl whom Neil had loved had clearly been, she thought, her own mouth firming in interminable resentment. Well, she could handle anyone who loved himself enough to be cast in bronze!

'Do you have an appointment?'

'No.'

'Then I'm sorry,' the accented voice answered, not sounding sorry at all, 'Signor Rossetti isn't seeing anyone today.'

A cold feeling of defeat washed over Chelsea, but then anger rose swiftly inside of her, tingeing her cheeks pink. 'Oh, he'll see me,' she assured the woman with a determination that surprised even herself. 'Is he in?'

'*Sì.* But—'

'Then tell him it's Julian Rendell's fiancée—and that I insist.'

For a moment the receptionist looked stunned, as though no one had ever dared to challenge the wishes of her eminent employer before. But then coolly she breathed, 'I'm sorry. Signor Rossetti made his orders very clear. But if you would like to make an appointment . . .'

With a swivel of her chair she was reaching for a diary, but Chelsea was already making for the steps.

'*Signorina! Signorina!*' The receptionist's angry en-
treaties went unheeded as Chelsea dived into one of the
lifts, the call she heard the woman making, before the doors
glided closed, obviously, from the urgency of her tone, an
instruction to someone to intercept her.

Making a snap decision, Chelsea pressed the button for
the top floor. Well, wouldn't this gargantuan god of fashion
and fragrance hold court at the very top? From the arro-
gance of that bust it seemed that this Milanese millionaire
gloried in power, in being king, she decided derogatorily
over more than a small twinge of nerves before the lift
purred to a sudden halt.

She was in a pale-carpeted lobby, with fringed palms
luxuriating in the light from windows that afforded panoramic views over the city. In the distance she could see the
monumental cathedral with its forest of marble turrets. She
wasn't, however, in any mood for sightseeing.

Instinctively, she was heading for a door on her left when
it suddenly opened, the tall man who emerged, and now
stood in front of it, arresting her with the sheer impact of
his masculinity.

Handsome was too commonplace a word to describe him,
and anyway it could never have embodied the force and
hard self-assurance in those Latin features, in the grim, implacable set of his mouth and jaw.

The dark, impeccable suit encased a physique of lean,
hard strength, such as might have belonged to an athlete—
or a bodyguard; the shining sable of his brushed-back hair
was only redeemed from harsh severity by a sprinkling of
grey at his temples—though he was probably only in his
early thirties. There was a lurking menace about him,
though, burning through that raw sexuality, and something
else—something in that superior regard of her that was
almost familiar, Chelsea sensed, before dismissing the
notion as impossible.

'You're looking for someone?' His voice was smooth and
deep, his English perfect with only the trace of an accent,
which provided little comfort as he took one step towards

her; the fact that he'd spoken in her own language was not too surprising either when it was clear from his intimidating stance that he had been warned about the English girl who had gatecrashed the usual channels of entry.

'I demand to see Mr Rossetti.' She wasn't quite sure how she was standing her ground in the face of such threatening calm and she saw a humourless smile touch the rather ruthless line of his mouth at her outward display of courage.

'Demand?' Head tilted, he gazed cynically down at her from his superior height, that hard power of his appeal unsettling her as she continued to guard the closed door. His arm was like a steel barrier across the frame. 'And what business have you with him that gives you liberty to flout all the security procedures of this building and come up here as if you had every right?'

'It's personal,' she supplied, her tongue coming nervously across her lips in spite of her chin-high air of defiance, because he was about the most dynamic-looking man she had ever met. His eyes were hard and sharp, amazingly dark.

'Really?' He leaned back against the door, folding his arms in a deceptively relaxed pose, and now his lips curved with a startlingly sensual charm. 'Are you suggesting he's been up to something that no one else should know about?'

She wasn't one to blush easily, but now she did, feeling those glimmering jet eyes tugging insolently over her creamy silk two-piece and red camisole.

'I—I told you—it's personal,' Chelsea reiterated, stammering, her sudden movement to force the issue bringing her disconcertingly aware of his well-honed reflexes when all he did was straighten swiftly—ready to remove her forcibly, she decided, swallowing at the thought of being dragged physically out of the building by him.

'And it seems you, young lady, need educating as to exactly who Mr Rossetti is,' he advised her, with mockery still playing around that cynical mouth.

'If you mean how *important* he is,' she flung back emphatically, 'personally I don't give a brass farthing!' Hadn't he ruined her wedding, humiliated her in front of her family and friends, besides destroying her cousin's career—and nearly his life—five years ago? 'I came here to speak to him—not to one of his watchdogs!' And with her blonde hair moving softly as she dipped her head towards the door that he was guarding she said, 'I take it he's in there. So if you don't mind I'd appreciate it if you'd please stand aside and let me pass!'

Surprisingly he complied then, displaying impeccable courtesy as he opened the door to allow her into that inner sanctum, only it wasn't an office, as she'd first thought. It was, presumably, the company boardroom, and it was deserted, save for the man she sought.

More impressive and imposing even than that bronze in the main lobby, he was staring down at her from a carved-framed study in oil!

Hearing the door close, she swung round. The watchdog was standing there with a twist of satisfaction on his lips and Chelsea felt a rush of anger, overlaid with the smallest measure of fear.

'All right, you've had your fun. Now let me speak to Paolo Rossetti.'

A dark, masculine hand gestured towards the left-hand wall. 'Then speak away.'

He was expecting her to address a painting! She shot him a wary glance, wondering if he was getting some weird kick out of playing this game with her, but there was no mockery on that ruthless mouth now, just cold, intimidating intent.

Her gaze flew from the painting above the long table to the man by the door and back to the painting again, then coolly she heard him explain, 'My father. But you might have difficulty speaking to him as he's been dead for the past eleven years. So, unless you're capable of sending messages to the spirit world, *signorina*, I'm afraid any communication you might wish to make is going to be with me.'

Flummoxed, Chelsea swallowed to ease a suddenly dry throat, her hand going unconsciously to its throbbing hollow. Of course, she could see the likeness now. That high, aristocratic forehead and the prominent cheekbones. That same wide mouth. There was no flaw, though, to lessen the flagrant masculinity of this man, no self-love, she suspected, to weaken that intimidating iron authority. 'You mean . . . *you're* . . .'

He dipped his head with purely superficial courtesy. 'It always caused confusion—bearing the same name—and my father was always prone to revel in grandiosity. I, myself, prefer a less . . . exaggerated profile. So you see, *signorina*, I'm no watchdog.' She was barely aware of him moving towards her, only of the ominous echo of his slow strides over the polished floor. 'But I do bite—and hard.'

And she had just felt the incisive edge of those metaphorical teeth, she realised shuddering, too stunned by the further realisation of just what his revelation meant to feel too embarrassed by what she had called him outside.

This, then, was the man whom Neil had been so cruelly reduced by, not that bronze sophisticate who even then— five years ago—would have had no powers beyond those of a harmless painting! This man, who looked polished and yet untamed, whose eyes seemed almost to hold a constrained rebellion in their depths, was the man with the ruthless power—power she knew only too well yet which she had never imagined would be backed not only by youth but by such hard, uncompromising strength.

Resentment overcoming shock, she found her tongue now, to demand, 'What have you done with my fiancé?' She was startled by the tremor that laced her query. She wasn't afraid of him, was she? Afraid? No, she thought. Affected? Yes. And by the hard, compelling force of his personality.

'Your fiancé?'

For a moment a line creased the high, olive brow, and a little more impatiently she said, 'Julian Rendell. What have you done with him?'

'Done with him?' He laughed, and those very perceptible teeth showed splendidly white against his

Mediterranean skin. 'What are you imagining I am—some sort of godfather? I can assure you, *signorina*, Julian Rendell came here entirely of his own free will.'

'Then where is he?' She sent a puzzled glance around her, unable to understand why, if Julian had come here willingly, he hadn't contacted her. She still couldn't get the notion out of her head that he was in some sort of trouble. 'You sent your private plane for him. I don't see how his coming here could possibly be self-motivated.'

'Why not?' His hands were in his pockets, causing the expensive cloth of his trousers to pull tautly across his lean hips. 'Because settling his obligations to me meant more to him than the idealistic fantasy of marriage?'

There was raw cynicism in his remark, but Chelsea was only aware of its implication. So he knew that they had been getting married yesterday!

'What do you mean?' she uttered, angry, puzzled. 'What obligations? Surely any outstanding matters he had with you could have waited at least until after we'd come back from our honeymoon?'

He rocked back on his heels, his face a mask hewn out of marble. 'Not when those obligations have been initiated by some suspected moral misdemeanour.'

'Suspected moral...' Her voice tailed off, lost in the hard acoustics of the long room. Aware of a couch behind her, she sank down onto it, her legs feeling like blancmange. 'What do you mean?' she queried shakily after a moment. 'Julian would never do anything immoral...unprofessional... And if you knew him like I do you'd know he's much too principled for that!'

'Such loyalty!' It was there again—that hard-edged cynicism, mocking the very essence of everything which despite the example of her parents' relationship—perhaps even because of it—she still clung to, still needed to believe in.

With colour returning to her cheeks, she said more heatedly, 'Anything less would hardly constitute a very good basis for marriage, would it, Mr Rossetti?' Absently, she wondered if he was married—had children. If not, then that powerful attraction would guarantee his influence over women—most women, she thought grudgingly. She couldn't imagine a man like him ever being content to sleep without his appetite fully appeased.

'Oh, I couldn't agree more.' Unsettlingly, his eyes followed the path of sunlight that was streaming in through one of the long windows, making a pale halo of her hair. 'But even the most wide-eyed individual can sometimes be blinkered, Miss...'

Trying not to acknowledge how beautiful his own eyes were, Chelsea swallowed, hesitant to tell him her name. She knew that Julian had never divulged to him that he was in any way connected with Neil Adamson, and, though she didn't feel too inclined to look after Julian's interests after what he'd done, wisely she murmured, 'Adams. Chelsea Adams,' and wondered now what he had meant by that last remark about being blinkered. Blinkered to what? Julian's character?

He'd let her down badly, it was true. Nevertheless, the man's words made her bristle, and tautly she demanded, 'I'd like to see him, please.'

'Would you?' His smile mocked her boldness. 'So you can lick his wounds? Would such loyalty prevail...through anything? Even through transgression? Through infidelity? Or is this engagement a totally open book—with no secrets hidden?'

What on earth was he talking about? She frowned. 'What's that supposed to mean?'

'You obviously don't remember.'

This time his mouth took on a coldly sardonic twist, and she dragged in a breath as, suddenly, he stooped to rest his arm on the back of the couch just above her shoulder, his nearness conveying such threateningly sensual messages to her that she shrank back, only just avoiding contact with that impeccable sleeve.

'Think back nine months. That three-day conference in Rome. You were staying at the hotel with Rendell—were, I believe, already wearing his ring. Yet when I saw you that last night, while the party was going on, you were not only coming out of that bedroom with another man but bragging about your conquest for the world to hear!'

So that was where she had seen him before—at the Rossetti conference! That was why he'd seemed familiar—not just because of the subtle likeness to his father! She hadn't wanted to go to that conference—even just for the social side—and she had only agreed to because Julian had assured her that Paolo Rossetti wouldn't be there. But he had been—briefly; vaguely now, she remembered Julian telling her that afterwards. And Paolo Rossetti had seen her coming out of that room with Julian's brother.

Murray and his wife had flown over for that last night, attended the party, and stayed on afterwards so that the four of them could enjoy a short break together.

She had slipped upstairs with Murray, their reasons for leaving that party innocent enough, and Chelsea remembered his embarrassment, his uneasy joke, as they'd come out of the bedroom, about Christine never believing them if she'd come up and caught them then.

She still didn't know whether it was the strength of the cocktails that she had been drinking, Murray's awkwardness or just a release of her own tension that night, but, aware of someone coming as she'd stepped into the corridor, she'd known a sudden, wicked desire to shock, and laughingly she'd thrown back over her shoulder, 'She wouldn't if she knew my sole intention was to get you up here tonight, Murray!'

And Paolo Rossetti had heard it! The man in the corridor! Whose stripping regard as he'd passed had made her giggle with sudden embarrassment at her shameless remark. Paolo Rossetti, who was accusing Julian of goodness knew what, and who thought that she was no better than a tramp! Little wonder he had had no respect for her prospective marriage!

If she could have flung his arm away she would have, but common sense warned her not to. Nevertheless, she had no intention of explaining to a man like him!

Her lashes drawn down to conceal the way his closeness and his very masculine cologne were impinging on her senses, she uttered coolly, 'I didn't realise my morals were under question here. I believe it's Julian's integrity that you'd like me to believe is suspect.' She met his eyes now, their unfathomable dark depths causing a shocking flame of something hot and elemental to burn along her veins, and she saw a smile touch his lips, almost as though he knew.

'I'm not asking you to believe anything.' Unsettlingly, those beautiful eyes fell casually to her lap, and in an unconscious gesture Chelsea brought her right hand over the diamond and ruby cluster adorning the third finger of her left, glad that she hadn't torn the ring off yesterday along with her wedding gown, as she so nearly had, if only for the fact that it spared her any further derogatory comments from this despicable man.

'Let me see him,' she insisted, refusing to be intimidated.

The quirk of an eyebrow seemed to mock her renewed confidence, but at last he straightened, allowing her to breathe freely again.

'Come.'

She had to pass close to him as he held the door open for her, and felt again the tug of his terrifying magnetism, so that she couldn't look at him as he guided her along the corridor. She wondered afterwards if it had been a touch of sadism on his part that had made him insist she follow him down five flights of stairs past a maze of offices, through the throbbing hive of enterprise that formed the pulse of his empire.

'This way.' He led her through a door and they were in another lobby—the entrance to a private apartment, she realised as he let her into a luxurious yet practically appointed suite.

'Aren't you coming in?' she asked tartly. 'Just in case we try and escape out of the window?'

'And witness the tender reunion?' His mouth displayed stone-hard cynicism. 'Somehow,' he said, 'I think the hypocrisy of it would be more than I could stomach.'

She swung round, a retort dying on her lips as she saw the door already closing behind him, leaving her to meet Julian alone.

He was slumped in one of the easy chairs in the huge sitting room, but leaped up when he saw her.

'Chelsea!' Casually dressed, the top button of his shirt unfastened, he looked shaken, hot and weary after the cool, impeccable elegance of the other man. 'What are you doing here?'

'What do you think I'm doing here?' she uttered poignantly.

'I know. I'm sorry, darling.' His hand lifted to his sandy hair, raked agitatedly through it. 'I really am sorry about yesterday—but I had no choice. I know I've got a lot of apologising to do to a lot of people, but I would have been there if I could. You do believe that, don't you?'

'Would you?' How could she be sure? She didn't know anything any more—what any of this was about. 'Why didn't you turn up?' she asked, hurting unbelievably. 'How could you leave me like that, in front of all those people, without a word...? What's going on?'

Julian's jaw clenched as he reached for her, catching her tightly to him. She could feel the tension in him, smell the faint scent of perspiration on his body. 'I've been put in a hell of a spot. Didn't Rossetti tell you?'

'He...he only said that there had been some moral misdemeanour,' she said, her voice cracking as she disentangled herself from his tight clasp. 'What does he mean? What moral misdemeanour?'

Julian's mouth pulled down one side. '"Moral misdemeanour"?' He laughed harshly, making Chelsea flinch. 'That's a polite way of putting it!'

'What do you mean?' Puzzlement etched tense lines on her delicate features as Julian moved away from her, then swung to face her again.

'I mean that his very precious, spoilt little niece has got herself pregnant and decided to point the finger at me.'

'*What?*' It was like being hit by a stone wall.

'*You're* surprised,' he said drily, while she was still trying to digest the news. 'Not half as surprised as I was! She's little more than a child—seventeen to be precise—but somehow she's managed to convince Rossetti that the baby she's carrying is mine.'

'Yours? But how can she? I mean, unless you...' Chelsea's sentence tailed off. It was all too bizarre—too divorced from the happy relationship with the man she had always trusted, believed herself to be marrying.

'Unless I what?' he challenged her roughly. 'Went to bed with her?'

The hard, hurting doubt in her eyes said it all. How could she have believed yesterday morning when she'd been on her way to the church that today she'd be here in Milan, asking him a question like this, she thought, and recoiled from his angry, 'Of course I didn't! Oh, all right, I'll admit I took her out once—'

'What? Since we've been engaged?'

'It was nothing like that,' he ground out. 'It was a couple of months ago...not because I fancied her or anything. She'd been looking forward to going to the opera and at the last minute Paolo couldn't take her. I thought it would be good for business if I stepped in. I went riding with her the next day, too, but I certainly had no other designs on her, and I certainly didn't lay a finger on her—not with Rossetti as her uncle.'

'Is that the only reason?'

'Oh, for heaven's sake, Chelsea! No, of course it isn't.' He was pacing the high-ceilinged room like a caged animal. 'One—I don't go to bed with rebellious seventeen-year-olds, and two—I would have hoped you would have credited me with a bit more integrity than that.'

She wanted to, but she was having difficulty coming to terms with all he was saying. She should have been in Paris now, on her honeymoon, not standing here in this ruthless millionaire's apartment, questioning the fidelity of the man she loved!

'You've got to believe me!' His tone was as urgent as the sudden, painful grip of his hands on her upper arms. 'Do you really think I'd mess around with another girl when I was going to marry you? *Chelsea*!' He almost shook her as she glanced away from him, staring sightlessly down at the sunlight striking fire from the polished mahogany of an expensive hi-fi cabinet.

She wanted to believe him—of course she did. But she still couldn't forgive him for not turning up yesterday. Which he would have, surely, she thought, if there hadn't been any truth in those allegations?

'I'm *sorry*,' he emphasised then, his arms falling away from her. 'I'm really sorry for not turning up. I just hoped I could get things sorted out before getting you involved.'

'Before . . .' She stared at him incredulously. 'How could I not be involved? I'm your fiancée, remember?' she breathed, unable to keep the sarcasm out of her voice. 'I think that entitles me to some rights—some share of your confidence. Unless, of course, it's true—'

'Of course it isn't!'

'Then why did you feel you had to come running when he snapped his fingers—accused you of it?'

'I didn't come running. I just thought it best to get this thing sorted out right away, not march down the aisle with it hanging over us, and he hasn't actually personally accused me of anything—he's not that stupid. Anyway, he's only doing what any guardian of a seventeen-year-old who's got herself pregnant would probably do—'

'You're defending him?' She exhaled, amazed. 'When you know what kind of man he is? What he did to Neil?'

'Neil? For heaven's sake! You didn't bring that up, did you?' Julian had turned quite pale. 'You didn't say anything out of turn, did you? Tell him who you were?'

'And what if I did?' She didn't think she could take much more, and wondered what Julian would say if she told him she had called his precious client a watchdog.

She caught his horrified 'Oh, God!' as he swung away from her, clutching his neck with a tense hand. 'This is my livelihood, Chelsea! *Our* livelihood! Our future! Any dealings he had with Neil are in the past. I've deliberately never mentioned knowing your cousin for all the embarrassment it could cause. So don't you say anything about him or anything that could connect you with him, or we can probably kiss goodbye to the best client Frost and Rendell will ever be likely to get, and that could put our future well and truly up the creek!'

'You couldn't be more up the creek than you are at the moment!' she accused him bitterly, his ingratiating attitude towards the Italian infuriating her, especially after what the man had done. 'Don't worry, I lied about my name!' she breathed, hating being underhanded about anything, even with someone she despised. 'And what about me? Doesn't it matter to you that he actually prevented us from getting married yesterday?' she enquired stingingly. 'Doesn't that mean anything to you?'

She had to repress the sob tearing at her throat and wondered if the doubts she'd been harbouring recently about her forthcoming marriage stemmed primarily from Julian's commitment to Paolo Rossetti.

'Of course it does.' He came back to her then, put his arms around her. 'You mean more to me than anything in the world. You must know that.'

Only she didn't. And that was the trouble. She wanted to be loved madly, passionately, only Julian was always too busy, always too preoccupied with work. She needed reassurance, especially after yesterday—reassurance that he loved her; that she *was* more important to him than anyone or anything else, including Paolo Rossetti.

But, giving her an absent-minded squeeze, he pulled back, saying only, 'Be a good girl for me and don't upset him, will you? I'm seeing Dulcibella in the morning—Paolo's making sure of that—and I intend to have it out with her in front of her precious uncle! In the meantime...' the faint trace of a smile appeared as his fingers strayed down

Chelsea's jawline ' . . . why don't we make the most of it here? Enjoy this wonderful luxury he's providing—?'

'No!' Her refusal was adamant. 'If you think I'm staying here with you after all this, you've got another think coming! You can stay here if you like, but I've already booked a hotel in town.'

'Charming!' Julian looked dumbfounded. 'If my own fiancée doesn't stand by me, what's Rossetti going to think?'

'In the circumstances,' she flung back, not caring what she said, 'I would have thought he'd be the first to understand!' Apart from which she wouldn't have taken any hospitality from Paolo Rossetti if her life had depended on it! 'You got yourself into this mess—you get yourself out of it,' she advised him, heading for the door. 'But there's one thing you'll never catch me doing, and that's staying under his roof!'

CHAPTER TWO

'You mean she admitted she made it all up—that she deliberately lied about the baby being yours?' Chelsea's voice rose disbelievingly. 'Of all the...! *Why*?' she felt the need to demand emphatically, flopping down, dumbfounded, onto the hotel room's single bed. 'Why pick on you?'

'Because, as I said before, she's a spoilt little brat. Oh, not by Rossetti—he's been strict enough with her—but by the influence she wields over people, just because of who she is. Apparently, she's been cultivating a pretty wild lifestyle and fooling around with an opportunistic young lad her uncle thoroughly disapproves of. When she suspected she was pregnant it seems that she was less daunted by the consequences of accusing me than by telling him the truth.'

'And you managed to persuade her to admit—?' The realisation of something Julian had just said sliced through the sentence she'd been uttering. 'What do you mean, "suspected"?' Somewhere outside in the corridor a door banged, keys jangled, the sounds intruding only absently on her confused thoughts.

'I mean that it was a false alarm. She's no more pregnant than you are,' Julian assured her with a grimace.

'And because of it she had her uncle drag you over here— for nothing!' Chelsea breathed, fuming. 'Stopped us from getting married! How could she—*he* accuse you of things like that without proof?' Her relief that Julian had been cleared was swamped by her anger towards Paolo and his niece. 'Couldn't you take him to court—sue him for defamation of character or something?'

Julian laughed. 'Sue Rossetti? Are you mad? And, to be fair, he didn't actually accuse me of it,' he reminded her, infuriatingly tolerant. No, sycophantic, she decided, bristling. 'He knows the rules.'

'He makes them, you mean.' Broodily, she looked up at her fiancé, wondering why he didn't appear as annoyed about the whole thing as she was. 'How can you talk about being fair when our lives have been turned totally upside down?'

'I know, sweetheart.' He gave her a lopsided grin, extending a hand to pull her to her feet. 'But it's all over now.'

At last her anger was being superseded by relief. 'Does that mean that we can go home now?' She wanted to—more than anything.

'Not for a day or two, darling. I wish we could go now, this afternoon, but it isn't possible. I'm sorry. As I'm over here, Rossetti's asked me to go over a few things with him regarding Dulcibella's trust fund, and that could take a day or two, but you spend some time looking around—you haven't seen Italy before. And perhaps I'll be able to join you for a few hours' sightseeing tomorrow when I'm through with business.'

'Are you sure you can spare the time?' Hurting, annoyed, she turned her head from the touch of his lips against her cheek. 'Rossetti! Rossetti! Rossetti! Perhaps you'd be happier marrying him instead!' she snapped, tugging out of his arms.

'Stop being unreasonable,' he advised her softly as he made to leave. Reaching the door, he added, 'You know that in the long run all my dealings with him are going to benefit us both.'

Perhaps they were, she thought as he left, but they weren't doing anything to help matters at present. After all, if it hadn't been for the Italian's intervention, they would have been in Paris on their honeymoon now.

A strange uneasiness stirred in her which she did her best to ignore. She'd do as he'd suggested, she decided resolutely five minutes later—go sightseeing, not sit around moping and have her time here ruined by that man Rossetti!

* * *

A trip through the square of small streets displaying Italy's most luxurious fashions provided a diversion from niggling thoughts, as did the bustling *piazzi* with their bars and clubs and crowded street cafés. But later, when she was strolling through the majestic interior of the great Gothic cathedral, they returned in force, worrying her as she gazed at the gruesome sculptured figure of St Bartholomew being flayed alive.

Wasn't she just so mixed up at the moment? she thought, shuddering at the sight of the figure who seemed to be glorying in his martyrdom. And it was hardly surprising, she told herself, after all that had happened during the past two days! Marrying Julian was the thing she most wanted, wasn't it? And those feelings she'd had over the past few weeks—what were they if not merely the prenuptial nerves that everyone about to embark on the commitment of their life usually suffered from?

Nevertheless, she ached to be able to have a heart-to-heart chat about them with someone—the one person who had always shared her problems, who had always been there to ease her worries—a friend and advisor when her parents' constant squabbling had been getting her down. Neil.

Dear Neil. As she abandoned the martyr for the awesome grandeur of carvings and stained glass, her thoughts wandered to the letter she'd received from him before the wedding.

From that communication she had been able to tell that he had finally picked up the pieces of his life—a life that had been brutally wrecked by Paolo Rossetti!

Neil had been a bright scholar and an equally successful businessman. He had had everything going for him that year when he had moved out to Milan. She supposed she had felt his leaving so acutely because, as he had lost his father while he was still quite small, her own parents had virtually fostered him so that his mother could work, and, being ten years older than Chelsea, he'd seemed more like a big brother to her than a cousin. They even looked alike, people used to say. Same fair hair and brown eyes, same slim build.

In spite of his humble beginnings, though, he'd done well. Everything he'd touched seemed to turn to gold. Seduced away by a warmer climate and an out-of-this-world opportunity, he'd looked like becoming the first Adamson millionaire when he'd opened a textile company in Milan. But then, five years ago, he'd met Paolo Rossetti, become friends—and then had got himself involved with a woman.

Chelsea wasn't sure of all the facts, only enough to know that it was a woman whom Paolo had been involved with too. The Italian hadn't been able to take that and he'd made Neil pay—ruthlessly and cruelly—using his incalculable power and shrewd business strategy to effect a takeover of Neil's company, succeeding not only in helping himself to everything her cousin had worked for but, as had probably been his intention, in driving him away from Milan.

Neil had returned to England an emotional and physical wreck, such had been the effect that Paolo's brutality had had upon him. And then, two years ago, when Julian, through one of Neil's old contacts, had landed the man as his client . . .

She gave a sad mental shrug as she stepped out of the cathedral into the dazzling sunlight. Neil had gone off to Canada, having never really forgiven Julian for that.

Her fiancé was in a buoyant mood when she got back to the hotel. She found him in the room that he had booked into, preparing to take a shower, and all the doubts that had been troubling her all afternoon started to subside as he caught her in his arms, holding her tightly.

'Um, you feel good,' he breathed, inhaling the scent of the Italian sunshine in her hair, his lips moving down her neck inside the collar of her red and white striped blouse. 'You look good too.'

Chelsea laughed. 'In a grubby shirt and jeans?'

She felt better already, nuzzling closer to his familiar warmth beneath his short, silk Paisley bathrobe, seeking the pleasurable sweetness of further intimacy that would make everything all right.

Firmly, though, he put her from him, reaching for the clean white shirt on the bed. 'Not now, Chelsea.' For Julian there was a time and a place for everything. 'We're going somewhere special tonight, so go and get yourself fixed up.'

And that excused his rejection of her affection—just, she thought wryly. Obviously he realised how tough this had all been for her too, and was making up for it by taking her somewhere nice.

She hadn't brought many clothes with her—and certainly nothing elaborate—as she hadn't known, when she had set off, whether she'd be catching the first plane back home. And so, after a welcome shower, she settled for a calf-length, red halter-neck dress that left the creamy slope of her shoulders bare, the wrap-around style emphasising her full, high breasts and tiny waist where it tied and dropping away to follow the soft curves of her hips and shapely legs.

'You look lovely,' Julian complimented her, unable, she was pleased to notice, to take his eyes off her when he called for her an hour later. His gaze approved the softly styled blonde bob, the subtle brown tones of her eye-shadow and the scarlet lipstick. 'What are you trying to do—make me lose my head?'

'I thought you already had!' she laughed, nestling into the arm he put around her, thinking how the dark grey suit enhanced his fair-skinned good looks as they headed for the lift.

One of Milan's famous yellow taxis bore them on a rather hair-raising journey across town, and as they grabbed one merciful breather while the cab waited at a junction Chelsea saw Julian glance at his watch.

'What time do we have to be there?' she queried, linking her arm automatically with his in the back of the taxi.

'Plenty of time,' he reassured her. 'I told Rossetti to expect us about half past.'

'Rossetti?' There was startled disbelief in the brown eyes turned towards his. 'Why?' Her voice was strung with poignant injury fast turning to annoyance. 'I thought we were going to be on our own.'

'I'm sorry, darling.' That seemed to have become one of Julian's stock phrases over the past couple of days, she thought peevishly as he went on, 'I wish we were too, but tonight's still partly business, as well as pleasure. I know how you feel about Paolo, but I thought even you would kick yourself at missing the chance to see inside a real fashion house, because that's where we're going—the House of Rossetti! And . . . well, there's something else. I thought I ought to warn you.'

'Warn me about what?' she asked, with a suspicion that wasn't usually part of her nature, feeling the judder of the taxi as it started pulling away.

'The man wants to discuss a few new proposals with me over the next couple of weeks—as well as requiring my advice over certain negotiations with a silk factory he's buying into in Como—and he thought it would be a good opportunity to expedite things while I'm here in Italy. He's got a villa in one of the resorts up there—right on the lake— and he's asked us both up to stay with him while the deal's going through.'

'He's *what*?' Chelsea looked at him aghast. 'I hope you said, Thanks, but no thanks!'

'I couldn't.' Julian's tone was conclusive. 'He's my client—and a hell of an important one. He said it'll be a good way of mixing business with pleasure and, for us, the added bonus of a holiday in compensation for the one we've had to forgo in Paris.'

'That's big of him!' Stupidly, she felt the burn of angry tears behind her eyes. First their evening together taken away, now this . . . 'Is that what he said it would be—*compensation*?' It was a tart little utterance, torn from her unappeasable dislike of the man.

'No. Not exactly.'

She hadn't thought so. She couldn't imagine that arrogant Italian using such self-deprecating words as 'sorry' and 'compensation', admitting he had been wrong.

'You know I couldn't justifiably take anything from that man after what he did to Neil,' she said, trying to make him understand, and added emphatically, 'I couldn't *do* it! Apart from which, if you think I'm going anywhere where I might have to encounter his obnoxious niece after all the lies she told about you, you're mad!'

'Chelsea, for heaven's sake!' Exasperation had crept into Julian's voice. 'He's specifically invited the two of us, and it isn't going to look good for me or the firm if you refuse. Dulcibella isn't going to be there. He gave me his word. And I know you think I'm only considering the business side of things, but I'm not. I'm thinking of the two of us. We'll be together. That's all that counts. And it isn't as though it's going to hurt you, is it, going along with what he wants?'

Those blue eyes were unusually pleading, and sceptically she wondered what was disturbing him most: the prospect of informing his client of her refusal, or his having to spend two or three weeks in Italy without her.

'No,' she said adamantly, fed up with the way he was treating her, always putting her last. 'You go if you have to, but I'm going home as planned!'

Fortunately, their arrival at their destination precluded any further discussion of the topic for the time being, and as they mounted the steps, entered through the revolving glass doors of the imposing House of Rossetti, Chelsea's immediate problems were swept aside by the total regality of her surroundings.

It was like stepping into another world. Indoor fountains cascaded like ribbons of silk through the luxury of the pleasingly air-conditioned foyer, their sound metallic above other sounds—the voices of other guests arriving, of the echo of their own footsteps over the marble floor.

Luxuriant plants grew lushly beneath a domed glass ceiling through which the hot, Italian sun would be allowed

to filter during the day, and on every side the faces of the
world's most beautiful women pouted down at her through
the eyes of the camera—famous models she'd seen staring
up at her from the front pages of glossy magazines, wearing
unaffordable creations from the dreams—pure fantasies—
of the most sought-after designers.

'See...? I told you you wouldn't have wanted to miss
this opportunity.' Julian was smiling smugly at her obvious
appreciation of her surroundings. 'Tonight they're cel-
ebrating the launch of the new range of Rossetti cosmetics—as well as a new perfume.' His mouth pulled in a
rather wry gesture. 'It's named after his niece, by the way.'

'Dulcibella?'

'I'm afraid so, Miss...Adams.'

Guiltily reminded of the name that she had given him,
Chelsea froze as Paolo came towards them, answering her
wide-eyed query. Her heart, when it resumed beating again,
did so with rapid momentum as she tried not to acknowledge consciously the utter magnetism of the man.

She hadn't seen him since he had left her with Julian in
the suite the previous day, keen as she had been to get away
from the place and take a cab back into town. If she had
thought Julian looked good earlier, though, in his tailored
dark suit, then that thrusting executive image was tran-
scended by a style and elegance that she had never in her
twenty-two years seen paralleled.

On any other man that light beige suit might have looked
too showy, but, combined with a pristine white shirt and
subtle cream and brown tie, it only made one aware of the
man who was wearing it, the colour enhancing the pure
olive of his skin, the grey-peppered ebony of his hair. And
the very flawlessness of that expensively cut cloth only emphasised the strength of his virility.

'I'm glad you could both come,' he said, his manners as
impeccable as his clothes. 'Though I apologise if the timing
is rather inapt. I can only say it's rather unfortunate for
you, *signorina*, that this launch is primarily to release
Dulcibella.'

She laughed—a small, high, sound strung with unaccountable nerves. 'On the contrary, Mr Rossetti, I would have thought it was more unfortunate for you.' A line deepened between his eyes and she was aware of the sudden hardening of those glittering irises resting on the softer brown of hers, but she pressed on anyway. 'Doesn't the name mean sweetly beautiful?' Her smile was as saccharine as the adjective that she had impregnated with sarcasm. She had looked the name up once, when Julian had casually mentioned Dulcibella in passing.

A ghost of a smile touched the man's lips as he dipped his head in the subtlest gesture.

'Touché,' he said softly, displaying impeccable charm, but she wasn't fooled. She knew only too well the dangerous streak that lurked behind that urbane façade and which common sense told her she'd be a fool to tamper with, but she couldn't help herself. He'd as good as wrecked Neil's life and he wasn't going to do the same with hers!

Beside her she heard Julian cough, awkwardly, aware of the unmistakable tension in the air.

'Chelsea's spent the afternoon looking at Milan.' It was an obvious attempt to ease the awkwardness between her and Paolo Rossetti, she realised, noticing the cool mockery touching that Latin mouth, as though he too knew what Julian was doing; but he allowed himself to swallow the bait all the same.

'Really?' Those eyes that had skimmed briefly over Julian were resting disturbingly on Chelsea again. 'What did you think of it?'

As if he cared! 'It's very nice,' she responded coolly, knowing that he was just making conversation—the hospitable host. 'Not what I expected at all.'

'And what did you expect?'

He was putting on a good show of looking genuinely interested, Chelsea thought, answering tightly, 'Something a little less modern—a little more Italian.'

The man laughed, looking disgustingly vibrant. 'It isn't a city to fall in love with, although every conqueror in history has attempted to get his hands on it. Have you been inside the cathedral?'

'Yes.' She didn't want to be here, making polite conversation with him—this man who had treated her cousin so brutally. She wished he would show them through the double doors into the room where other people were headed, leave them and attend to his other guests.

'She not only went inside it—she's been on the roof!' Julian was informing him, to her dismay, obviously keen to improve relations between her and his prestigious client. 'If there's a summit to be conquered, Chelsea will conquer it. Isn't that so, darling?'

Julian's patronising tone made her flinch, though she gave him a rather forced smile, feeling the burn of the other man's gaze like fire across the bare slope of her shoulders.

'Really?' Behind that cool remark there was some hidden innuendo that was too subtle for her to grasp, but for a moment a powerful magnetism kept her from answering, or even glancing away. Then Julian coughed again—that slightly awkward cough—and Paolo's smile was like a curtain closing on an unfinished play. 'With one hundred and thirty-five spires it's a sight one shouldn't miss.'

It took a few moments for Chelsea to realise that he was still talking about the cathedral.

'The Duomo.' He made the word sound sacred and sensual, if that was possible, all at the same time. 'There's no better view of the city—up there with all those marble saints looking over you—and on a clear day the eye will take you all the way to the Alps.'

Sudden tension gripped her, her cheekbones appearing high and prominent in the fine structure of her face.

'Yes,' she uttered, and so stiffly that she saw Paolo frown. But then he didn't know that for her those mountains merely symbolised his last act of treachery against her cousin— didn't know because he wasn't even aware of who she was.

'You didn't tell me about that, love.' Coming from a distance, it seemed, Julian's comment was a comfort for being so totally mundane. She wanted him to reach out, put his arm around her, protect her from the silent hostility that she was engendering in the other man. She could feel it, see it in his eyes. It wasn't like Julian, though, to be demonstrative in public, and anyway, Paolo was suggesting now that they go inside, enjoy the champagne, though a prickly feeling down the back of her neck told her that he was still watching her as she allowed Julian to lead her away.

'Well, that's over with,' Julian remarked, and hopefully she wondered if his unconcealed relief meant that they wouldn't be seeing much of their host for the rest of the evening. 'You could have appeared to be a little more friendly to him.'

They were in a banqueting room of sorts, the glistening chandeliers reflecting in the floor-to-ceiling mirrors, the elaborate architecture and sumptuous furnishings a fitting backdrop for one of the most celebrated names in the world of fashion and beauty.

'Wasn't I?' She slanted a look of mock innocence towards her fiancé. 'I thought I was niceness itself under the circumstances!'

'Oh, come on, Chelsea . . .!'

She could see that he was getting steamed up, and a full-scale row with him was the last thing she wanted—not in public, and certainly not over Paolo Rossetti! Making an effort, therefore, she said, 'Did he inherit all this?' A toss of her head embraced the elegant seat of an obvious multi-million-pound empire. 'He said something about his father dying over eleven years ago,' she remembered from her embarrassing blunder at his offices the previous day. Yet, from the many photographs dotted around the place and a marble bust that she had noticed in the reception area this evening, the presence of Paolo's father still seemed pretty much in evidence.

'Paolo owns it all, lock, stock and barrel,' Julian was responding with unconcealed awe. 'Unlike his father, though, who lived, breathed and slept for design, Paolo prefers to leave the fashion side of the business to a team of experts. He isn't really involved with that side of things;

he's more on the perfume and cosmetics side, and works
as hard as anybody else—probably harder up there at the
helm, although he could take a back seat and happily do
nothing but watch the millions roll in if he chose to, but
he's got too much energy and drive to simply relegate
everything to everybody else.'

'Perhaps he likes the feeling of dictatorship,' she suggested
waspishly, refusing to be impressed.

'Not so much that he doesn't have time to play—and as
hard as he works,' Julian appended, ignoring her derogatory comment. 'Why the sudden interest anyway? You
never wanted to know anything about him before—let alone
discuss the man.'

She gave a nonchalant little shrug. 'Just curious,' she
said, sounding impartial, but she still couldn't help asking,
'And Mrs Rossetti?'

From out of the milling crowd a waiter appeared with
champagne on a silver tray. They both took a glass. 'His
mother lives in Sicily.'

'No, I mean his wife.' Chelsea put the fine flute to her
lips, felt the bubbles tickling her nose. 'Isn't he married?'

'Are you kidding? With every woman he meets wanting
to fall into bed with him? Why tie himself down?'

'Thanks!' she breathed, with more than a little sarcasm.
'If that's how you feel about marriage, why are *you*
bothering?'

'Oh, come on!' He picked up her hand and kissed it. 'He
obviously hasn't met anyone like you yet, has he?' he said,
smiling. 'Now, let's try to enjoy ourselves. Forget about
Paolo.'

Fortunately the party progressed without any further
communication with their host. Once Julian excused himself
for a short period and Chelsea spotted him having a few
words with Paolo before the latter was drawn into conversation with a couple of older men standing nearby. Apart
from that, the dynamic perfumer seemed surrounded by a
throng of elegant guests all evening—most of them women!

Uninterested, she turned away, content to browse through the exquisite array of the latest beauty products, smiling a polite refusal as one of the lovely models tried to spray her with the latest Rossetti fragrance.

'Somehow I don't think it will be quite what the *signorina* would wear.'

The smooth Latin voice had spoken the words in English, and she swung round, looking up into those incredibly charismatic features.

'How right you are.'

A faint smile acknowledged the undisguised sting in her voice. 'I've been led to understand,' he said, 'that you don't intend joining Rendell at the villa.'

So Julian had already told him. 'No,' she said curtly, and, lifting challenging eyes to his, couldn't refrain from adding, 'Even if my plans for Paris might have been needlessly messed up, I've no intention of spending any more time in Italy than I have to.'

His chest lifted heavily beneath the pristine silk of his shirt. 'Still angry with me for robbing you of your marriage vows?'

'What on earth makes you think that?' Sarcasm dripped from her words. 'I enjoyed having my wedding ruined through some spoilt little schoolgirl's vicious lies! And what you did was a downright liberty. Neither your money nor your influence gives you the right to try and ruin other people's lives!'

'I wouldn't call ensuring the security of my niece exactly ruining anyone's life.' All charm had been swept from the hard structure of his face and his eyes were like penetrating steel. 'Your fiancé—as I believed at the time—had already done that for himself. So...' he threw out his hands, drawing her attention unwittingly to the lean elegance of his body beneath the impeccable suit ' ...I was misled. I wasn't to know that Dulcibella had lied.'

For a moment she caught a glimpse of some previously hidden emotion in the tautening of his jaw, in the fine creases of his eyes. He obviously cared a great deal about his niece. He had to, if he'd named his company's latest product after her. That much she could appreciate—if not his actions.

'That still gave you no right to—'

'To what? Drag your dearly beloved away from the altar?'

She ignored the derisive remark as he took her empty glass and replaced it with a full one from a passing tray. She flinched as his long, warm fingers accidentally touched hers.

'It was humiliating…' Damn! Why did he make her sound like a frog with laryngitis?

'And now instead of being locked in the clutches of connubial bliss you're here—in Italy—with me.'

Linking them both in the same breath with the intimacy that she and Julian should have been sharing now brought the blood rushing to her cheeks. She could smell the subtle musk of his aftershave lotion, feel the potency of his masculinity like some tangible threat.

'I don't think that's in particularly good taste!'

'It wasn't meant to be. But then you can't expect me to feel any particular sentiment for your prospective marriage, can you?'

He was referring to her infidelity with Murray that he believed he had witnessed, but before she could even consider denying any such unfaithfulness he went on, 'What's really galling you? The fact that Rendell put you second? That he sacrificed his sham of a wedding for his firm's more lucrative allegiance to me?'

God, the man was hateful! 'He had no choice!' she snapped, hating his scorn for an occasion which, despite her fears, she had longed for, looked forward to almost with reverence.

'No?' This with a doubting lift of brows. 'He's so anxious to keep in my favour that he'll do anything I ask.'

His opinion of her fiancé peeved her, especially since she couldn't deny that Julian had changed—become less fun-loving, almost totally obsessed with work—during the two years that he had been involved with the House of Rossetti.

'Exactly why are you marrying him?'

'*What*?' She couldn't believe he had the gall to be questioning her like this.

'Is it for his prospects, the style in which he'll be able to keep you? Because both you and I know it isn't for love, don't we?'

Her eyes were glittering with festering dislike as she threw back her head, her hair catching the light. 'Why else?' she breathed, not caring if she did reinforce his shallow estimation of her. A man like him would never believe anything good of anyone anyway!

'What did you do—' his voice was roughly scathing '—swap partners in that hotel? Or did you make sure Rendell was suitably occupied before sneaking upstairs with his brother?'

So he knew who Murray was, she realised, guessing that Julian must have told him at that conference. This was going too far, though, she thought, wondering how she'd ever managed to mislead him into thinking such sordid things about her.

Nevertheless, with lips that were tantalisingly scarlet she took a sip of her champagne, flashed him a bright smile and said, 'As you seem to know everything about me—you work it out.'

From the hard curve of his lips it seemed that he had already done that. 'You're as beautiful as I remembered you to be,' he said, his tone harshening. 'And twice as heartless. A beautiful, sexy, scheming little tramp.'

'That makes two of us, then, doesn't it?' she retorted, slamming her glass down on a nearby table, his remarks giving full rein to the five-year-long resentment and bitterness that she had had to endure towards this man. 'Aren't you rather mixing me up with your debauched little niece?'

For a moment his cheekbones seemed to stand out under the bronzed skin and his proud nostrils flared as he battled with a powerful anger, but that iron control won.

'Compared to you, Dulcibella's an angel!' he breathed, looking down at her as though she were something he wouldn't even want to stand on.

His contempt for her was frightening—excessively so—and she failed to understand why.

'Perhaps Rendell doesn't know about your little liaisons. Maybe I should acquaint him with the facts. I think, however, you'd prefer it if it was kept between the two of us. I would remind you, therefore, how much his company is depending upon my business, and a man with a spouse who chooses not to support her husband both professionally and socially is hardly a good risk...' his smile was merely a formality in the implacable hardness of his face '...as I'm sure you'll agree. I'm also sure that you'll want to do everything you can to minimise that risk. Therefore I would suggest you accept the invitation to accompany him to my villa with the good grace with which it was offered.'

What was he saying—that if she didn't Frost and Rendell's contract with him could go to hell?

Her lips tightening, she wanted to fling at him that he could tell Julian what he liked! That, after the way he had treated her, right at this moment she didn't really care if he did lose his precious custom!

A desire, though, to lash out at this man who had victimised her cousin, show him up for what he was, if that was possible, as payment for the way Neil had been treated, was stronger than any insubstantial threat that Paolo Rossetti cared to issue. And if she did as he was suggesting...

'Well?' he said coldly. 'Do we understand each other?'

'Perfectly.' She gave him a tight smile. 'Although, as you're so enamoured of my company—'

A loud crash followed by a momentary hush stopped her asking him why he was even bothering.

Somewhere near the Dulcibella stand someone had dropped a phial of the new and exclusive perfume. Relieved laughter preceded the hubbub of returning conversation,

and with the rich fragrance cloying in her nostrils Chelsea
glanced down, feeling a sensation ripple along her leg.

A shard of fine glass had grazed her leg just above her
ankle. She could see the run in her stocking, the pinprick
of blood seeping out from the wound beneath.

'I thought I'd find you here amongst the cosmetics.
Haven't ordered the entire range on show, I hope!'

Laughter laced Julian's voice and Chelsea plastered on
a smile, never more glad to see him than at that moment,
as beside her she heard that deeper, more resonant voice
say, 'I'm afraid I've been monopolising all her time, but I
do believe I've managed to persuade her that a couple of
weeks at my villa will be exactly what she needs.'

She wanted to hit Paolo, cry out that the last thing the
Italian cared about was her needs or anybody else's, that
Julian had to be blind if he couldn't see what sort of man
Paolo Rossetti was. Hopelessly, though, she glanced down,
seeing the dark red staining her stocking.

'Oh, *no*!'

Julian didn't hear her despairing little groan, but *he* did.
As she drew her knee up to check the extent of the damage,
a folded white handkerchief was being clamped over the
bleeding wound, the masculine hand shockingly strong
around the feminine slenderness of her ankle, that pale
sleeve a startling contrast against the dark, sheer gloss of
her stocking.

He couldn't have missed her short, sharp gasp, and like
an animal acting solely on the strongest instinct to survive,
she shrank involuntarily away. Twisting on her other heel,
she stumbled against him, the shocking impression of rock-
hard strength beneath the deceptive softness of his jacket
filling her with such primitive and unwelcome impulses that
she felt as though she was fighting for breath. She drew
back so fast when he released her that she almost stumbled
again.

'You'd better have this.'

'N-no, I'm all right.' Stammeringly, she recoiled from
taking the immaculate handkerchief, stained now with her

blood, and, snapping open her bag, rummaged agitatedly through it for a tissue.

'You've cut yourself? Are you all right, Chelsea?' Julian's voice came worriedly through the haze of her rampaging emotions as her trembling fingers dabbed hectically at the wound. 'You look awful. My God, you're shaking! What have you done?'

Damn Julian! 'I'm all right!' She didn't sound it. She could hear her voice cracking. 'C-could we go home? I—I've ruined my stocking. I feel such a mess.' She was babbling, her words tumbling out in a jerky, agitated stream.

'Well . . . if you want to . . .' He didn't. That was obvious. But to Paolo he added, 'You don't mind . . .?' Why did he make it sound as though he needed the man's permission, for heaven's sake? Couldn't Julian see that it was such deference to the man that made him such a tyrant?

She couldn't bring herself to look at Paolo as he murmured some assenting response. And then he said to her, 'Does the sight of blood always make you so queasy . . . Chelsea?'

His softly spoken statement willed her to look at him, the deliberate emphasis and sensuality with which he had breathed her name adding to the turmoil that was going on inside her.

'I—I'm sorry to be a nuisance,' was all she could utter, and mainly to Julian, as she was unable to lie and grasp the excuse that Paolo was offering her for her total lack of composure. He wouldn't have believed it anyway.

That cruelly mocking smile as he'd dipped his head in the subtlest acknowledgement haunted her even as she sat beside Julian in the taxi back to the hotel.

The man was despicable—manipulative and ruthless. She had always known that, without even having met him. Yet when she had fallen against him tonight, felt those steadying, unwelcome arms around her, she had experienced an intensity of excitement that was nothing if not sick—totally perverse.

She hated Paolo Rossetti! She reiterated it silently to herself, easing closer to the man beside her in an unconscious request for protection. But protection from what? How could he hurt her? She didn't know; she only knew that, unlike her cousin, she didn't intend giving him even half a chance!

CHAPTER THREE

THE sun beat hotly on Chelsea's face and bare arms as she ambled down the worn steps between the rows of tiny shops in the lakeside village, absorbing everything they had to offer: delicious trays of confectionery, glass and porcelain, framed prints, leather and silk. It was a window-shopper's delight—one that made her almost glad she had come.

Even Julian would have liked it, she decided, tucking the sketch-pad that she had just purchased under her arm and offering a bright smile to an elderly woman sitting in a doorway, face wrinkled and weathered, her gnarled hands working delicate lace.

But Julian was tied up with business, and had been since they had arrived yesterday from Milan, she thought wearily. She hadn't told him why she had changed her mind about coming here, or anything about Paolo's threats.

She glanced up at the bright scarlet of one of the geranium-clad balconies, smelling freshly baked bread and garlic and the powdery scent of a host of Mediterranean flowers.

So much for being together! That, however, had meant that Paolo had been tied up too, so that while she had seen little of Julian she'd seen even less of their host, which had to be some compensation at least.

The villa was a huge white, terracotta-roofed house with high arched windows enjoying a panoramic view of the mountains and the lake. The tall iron gates with their intimidating warning of guard dogs left no one in any doubt that one was entering a rich man's world—a world of luxury, defined on every one of its three floors by its rich, antique furniture, carved marble fireplaces, and by the graceful figurines that one would come across at random in the arched recesses throughout the house.

But it was luxury without ostentation, Chelsea had decided at once, grudgingly accepting that it was probably Paolo's combined good taste and appreciation of the classical that made her fall in love with the place almost immediately, situated, as it was, in perfect seclusion on the wooded hillside, a good walk from the village.

Now, experiencing a guilty relief at the absence of any car on the drive, she went straight up to her room—a luxuriously feminine room facing lakewards and plushly decorated in creams and peaches with its own private bathroom in peach marble. She didn't linger, however, but quickly substituted her sundress for a bikini, and, with a shirt thrown over the top, came down again across the sumptuous elegance of the hall.

'*Buongiorno*.' Smiling to Maria, the young maid, above the hum of the *lucidatrice* which was keeping the eternal shine on the marble floor, she made her way onto the terrace.

Oleander trees ran the whole length of the terrace, screening the long pool from the house, and after taking an invigorating swim in the refreshing blue water Chelsea settled down to sunbathe on one of the loungers.

Prominently positioned as the villa was, sounds drifted up to her from across the valley: the distant, plaintive peal of church bells, the sudden burr of a moped, the hydrofoil bringing tourists from the pretty resorts across the lake, its very approach seeming to whisper its more romantic Italian name. 'Aliscafo. Aliscafo. Aliscafo . . .'

Caught by a sudden pang of loneliness, her ears were suddenly attuned to the sound of footsteps on the flagstone terrace. Julian!

Her heart plummeted and then took up some crazy, irregular rhythm as she saw Paolo emerge from beneath the scented pink flowers of the oleanders.

'Good afternoon.' Wearing only dark shorts and a pale shirt unbuttoned to the waist, he came to a halt just in front of her. 'You're looking very relaxed.'

Shielding her eyes with her hand, Chelsea tried to ignore how virile he looked, standing there smiling down at her.

'Yes,' she responded stiffly, dragging her gaze away.

'I'm glad I returned. Are you going to be out here long?'

Why? Because he was enjoying the sight of her semi-naked body? she thought waspishly, feeling that heat of his gaze as tangibly as the sun over the three scanty yellow triangles of polka dots that served as a bikini. 'No.'

A quirk of an eyebrow said he'd felt that sharpness in her response. 'Do you find it insulting that I should be concerned you don't burn that tender English skin? It's rather too fair for our fierce Italian sun.' A greater heat stole over her as his observation seemed to give him licence to survey her soft, slickly oiled body. 'I'd think about covering those shoulders if I were you.' Almost like a statement of his own invulnerability, he was removing his shirt. His chest was beautifully bronzed, muscled, feathered with dark hair.

Disconcerted by the way she had misconstrued his earlier question, and how, as if he'd known her thoughts, he'd deftly put her in her place, Chelsea reached for her white cotton cover-up.

'Where's Julian?' She was very conscious of those dark-fringed eyes resting on her, conscious too of the way the cleft between her breast deepened as she slipped her arms into her shirt.

'I've sent him to negotiate more favourable terms on my interests in Como.' His smile seemed to mock her. 'Don't worry—he'll be back,' he promised cynically, making himself comfortable on another lounger.

Unwillingly, Chelsea's gaze followed the superb, masculine lines of his body. Long legs darkened by hair, a flat stomach and firm waist, a powerful chest and shoulders. He was almost perfect—but not quite. There was a jagged scar running down from his right shoulder towards his breastbone—what once would have been a very angry gash.

Her eyes lifted, met the dark scrutiny of his. She blushed, realising how transparent her curiosity must be, and quickly she said, 'Your English is perfect. You don't even have an accent—or hardly. Where did you learn it?'

His smile was perceptive. He knew that that wasn't what she had really wanted to ask. 'I had an English nanny,' he enlightened her. 'And I finished my education at Cambridge. My father wanted his sons to have every asset conceivable to take over his business.'

His sons? Of course, Dulcibella's father, she figured, feeling that edge to his voice. Well, she wasn't exactly enjoying *his* company either!

'And are all your guests treated to your company's latest products whenever they come to stay?' Her tone was as ascerbic as his had been. 'Or was it just for my benefit?' Her bathroom seemed to boast them all: soaps, talc, bath oils, and, on the shelf above the basin, that familiarly dark, elongated bottle of the exclusive perfume itself.

A frown knitted Paolo's brows. And, realising, he said, 'Maria must have put them there,' he said laconically. 'I'll have them removed.'

'Please—don't bother on my account,' Chelsea retorted. But she liked the shy yet efficient little maid so after a moment she added more congenially, 'It isn't necessary. I wouldn't want to do anything to upset Maria.'

Those broad shoulders shrugged as though he didn't care either way, and, unable to restrain her reluctant curiosity about him, she went on, 'Is your rather...*wayward* niece—' her voice held unrestrained sarcasm '—your only other family? Julian said you've got a mother in Sicily.'

'Yes.'

'Where are Dulcibella's parents? Or have they washed their hands of her?' She couldn't contain the cynical little sneer.

From the opposite lounger Paolo was looking at her with a hard, unsettling intensity. A bird sang through the suddenly charged silence that she couldn't account for, and the wind stirred the oleanders enough to catch a glimpse of the purple bougainvillaea that grew with striking contrast against the villa's white walls.

'They're no longer around.'

What did that mean? He looked so formidable suddenly that she didn't have the nerve to ask. Then, as if she had imagined it, some of the fierceness ebbed away and he was enquiring, 'What about you? Do you find it satisfying—operating computers in an insurance office?'

She couldn't remember telling him what she did.

'It's a living,' she said with a little shrug, guessing that Julian must have told him. 'Julian wanted me to work for him after we were married, but I don't feel that a husband and wife should work in the same office.'

'That depends.' Clearly he didn't entirely share her view. 'How long have you known Rendell? Where did you meet him?'

Those simple questions sounded interrogative almost, and she felt like throwing back, He was Neil's best friend. Neil Adamson, remember? My cousin. The man you reduced to a wreck! But calmly all she said was, 'Our parents were friends before either of us were born.'

'And if I hadn't intervened you would have been his wife now. And yet...' those thick eyelashes made shadows against the wells of his eyes as he cast a brief glance over her body '...you are not lovers.'

'I beg your pardon?' Shock had brought her upright on the lounger, two spots of bright colour deepening on her cheeks. 'I don't see that that's any business of yours!'

'I'm sorry.' He wasn't. Reclining there, arrogant in his manhood, he wasn't even looking at her now. He was gazing out in the direction of an impressive, palatial villa that she could see on the other side of the lake. 'I wouldn't even have mentioned it had Rendell not laid such emphasis on the two of you having separate rooms, saying that you would insist upon it...'

'And what's wrong with that?' Even before she had said it, she realised what he was thinking. It was her own stupidity in not putting him straight at the very beginning that earned her such a contemptuous look from him now.

'You sleep with his brother—and yet you keep the man you are going to marry panting like a thirsty jackal.' His laugh was harsh and crude. 'Does it turn you on, knowing he's being driven mad with frustration? Or does staying out of his bed keep him from suspecting the truth?'

She wanted to leap up and slap the derision off his cruelly contemptuous mouth, because the truth was that she had wanted her marriage to be special in every way. Most girls she knew slept around, but she hadn't, not even with Julian, believing that if she stayed, as her friends called her "boringly old-fashioned" her marriage might not deteriorate or turn sour as her parents' marriage had.

Her own mother had warned her often enough that sex clouded the judgement, that if she herself hadn't rushed into a relationship with Rupert Adamson, hadn't conceived Chelsea, she would never have married him, never have made the mistake that Chelsea had found herself paying for over and over all the time she was growing up. And though Julian had often tried to persuade her otherwise, she had stuck to her decision, never allowing their desire to go beyond pleasurable petting.

'Not everyone's got your problem,' she uttered icily instead. 'A warped, overdeveloped imagination!'

'Overdeveloped?' He laughed and sat up then. The sun was picking out the grey flecks at his temples; his hair was curling into the nape of his neck, ebony against bronze. 'I'm just totally fascinated by the whole arrangement—because if you had come that close to being my bride last week there's no way you would be anywhere now but in my bed.'

His mind-bending statement hung in the silence that stretched between them, resolute and unequivocal. A treacherous slick of something molten and intrinsic percolated through her bloodstream, making her pulse throb with that sick excitement that she had experienced before. Down on the sapphire water the ferry was departing, and she stared at its sparkling wake, trying to focus mentally on Julian's familiar features. With a surge of desperation she found it almost impossible.

'But I'm not *your* prospective bride, am I?' her discomfiture made her snap.

'More's the pity.' At least, that was what she thought he muttered under his breath. 'If you were, then with my... imagination and your lack of scruples...'

The sensuality in his innuendo took her by surprise, preventing her from firing back an immediate response.

Her eyes were guarded as she watched him slip off the lounger, move over to stand in front of hers. He was all too big, too male, too positively *Italian*! She had to force herself to drag her gaze past him, to the soft pinks and ochres of the houses down in the village with their terracotta roofs, a pulse beating furiously in her throat.

'Does he know your reactions go into panic mode every time another man comes within half a metre of you—every time *I* come within half a metre of you, Chelsea?' Those long dark hands were splayed casually against the narrow angles of his hips, bringing her gaze unwittingly across the dark shorts to his muscled, hair-covered thighs. 'You nearly had me fooled into believing you really were distressed when you cut your leg the other night. I know you certainly fooled Rendell. But both you and I know, don't we, that it was something more than just simple hostility that had you pulling out of my arms?'

Chelsea's throat seemed to clog and she swallowed—hard. Had he guessed at the frightening intensity of sensation that she had felt when she had stumbled against him, that she was—heaven help her!—battling with now?

'You're unbelievably conceited,' she uttered in a faltering voice.

'Perhaps,' he agreed, smiling that cool, contemplative smile. 'But if I'm not then there must be another reason—possibly—why you feel so uncomfortable with me.'

He had hit the nail on the head, his doubly accurate suspicion nearly stripping her of what composure she had left, but she refused to let it show.

'Perhaps you should take a swim,' she parried, flashing him an insincere smile.

'Only if you'll join me,' he said softly, with an equal insincerity of warmth.

'Get lost!' she breathed, with all the revulsion of her skin-crawling, inexplicable attraction to him, and, gathering up her sandals and sun-lotion, she made her hasty escape inside.

Miraculously she didn't see him again for the rest of the afternoon, nor Julian, for that matter.

She was lounging on her bed, absorbed in a traveller's guide to eighteenth-century lakeland villas when she heard Julian drive in, using Paolo's Ferrari until the hire car arrived—and revelling in it, she didn't doubt. After twenty minutes or so, however, when he hadn't come to find her, she made her way up to the room immediately above hers.

'Julian?'

He hadn't answered her knock but he was there, stuffing something into his briefcase as she peered round the door.

'Oh, it's you!' He looked hot and dishevelled and . . . what? . . . relieved, she thought curiously, to see her.

'Of course it's me. Who else did you think it was?' she said, with a half-smile, half-frown as she went automatically into his arms.

He laughed then. 'Hey! If this is the welcome I get I'll stay away more often,' he said approvingly, giving her a tight squeeze.

'Then why didn't you come up and see me as soon as you came in?'

'I . . . had things to do.' Too soon he was releasing her. He still seemed agitated, distracted, she thought as she watched him snap his briefcase closed, toss it down beside the chest of drawers. 'What have you been doing all day?'

As he started getting changed she told him about her walk and the ancient church in the village, mourning the warm familiarity of his arms. She always felt safe—not threatened or disturbed as she was by the other man's company—

when Julian held her close. And yet nor did she feel that depraved excitement . . .

'You've been sunbathing too—I can tell.' Coming back across the room, Julian put the brakes on her grossly unsettling thoughts with a finger on her rather glowing nose. Then casually he asked, 'Paolo been around at all?'

Chelsea hesitated, her breath shortening. 'This afternoon,' she said carelessly, that scene with him by the poolside, the things he'd said, still affecting her more than she wanted to be affected.

'I hope you were nice to him,' he said, eyeing her dubiously as he slipped into a clean, casual shirt.

Rebellion tightened her lips. 'Sure. I spent the afternoon telling him how wonderful he was and then did the dance of the seven veils for him!' she snapped, wondering just how Julian would react if he knew how rude she'd actually been to his client. And then, her curiosity too much to restrain, before she had even realised it she was asking, 'How did he get that scar?'

Julian's sandy brows lifted as he finished buttoning his shirt. 'Oh, so you've seen him naked, have you?'

'Hardly.' The negation accompanied a deprecating little grimace. If they had been discussing any other man she might have teased him about it, but she couldn't, disconcerted by the flush that she could feel staining her cheeks. 'He came out for a swim while I was sunbathing and I noticed it then.'

'Thank heaven for that!' Julian's hand was on his heart in mock relief. 'Search me,' he said more seriously then, putting his jacket carefully on a hanger. Everything always had to be tidy with Julian—everything always in its place. 'Why don't you ask him?' And with a sudden rare gleam of wickedness in his eyes he said, 'He probably took some kitten to bed who turned out to be a tigress—knowing his reputation with women.'

Only, one of those women had chosen Neil, and Paolo had made him pay, Chelsea thought with burning, long-festering resentment. He'd been brutal, merciless in his humiliation of her cousin, and she must never let herself forget that.

Fortunately they had the whole of the following day to themselves, and when Julian suggested that they dine out that evening—just the two of them—Chelsea was more than happy to agree, because the previous two evenings dining with Paolo had been a strain that she would much rather have done without. Not that he had allowed their meal-times to be monopolised totally by business.

Strangely, despite his low opinion of her, he had been careful to include her in the general conversation—asking for her direct views on matters, about the things she liked to do—so that she had felt compelled to respond. Which was, she supposed as she strolled down towards the village with Julian that evening, what had made the man such a powerful force in business—that uncanny talent for getting the best out of people, whether they wanted to give it or not!

'Paolo recommended this place a couple of days ago,' Julian told her as he escorted her into the luxurious hotel, guiding her out onto a canopied terrace overlooking the lake.

Reluctantly, she had to reinforce her view that the man had taste. Although mellowed in its grandeur, it was probably still the best hotel in the area. Here on the terrace, soft lights created a romantic atmosphere around tables laid for dinner, although these hadn't yet come into their own as it was still barely dusk. Stone urns stocked with bright flowers adorned the balustrade, and beyond, in the fragrant gardens, date palms, oleanders and willows sighed into the shadows where the terrace lights winked back at them from a rectangular pool.

'It's lovely,' she said appreciatively, happier for having spent a whole day away from Paolo. That morning, after the hired car had arrived, they had driven down to explore a neighbouring resort. Then, during the afternoon, they had come back and gone for a walk along the wooded headland, and tomorrow Julian had promised to take her to see that villa across the lake.

'Speak of the devil . . .' His surprised comment made her turn, curiosity turning to heart-stopping dismay as she saw Paolo, strikingly elegant in a dark lounge suit, sitting with a raven-haired beauty at one of the tables.

The briefest nod from him acknowledged their presence, though he gave no indication that they should join him—a thing over which Julian seemed rather put out as they sat down.

'He's obviously got far more interesting company,' Chelsea said carelessly, relief unable to counteract the inexplicable tension suddenly knotting her stomach. 'If he's got any decency at all he might possibly realise that we *do* want some time on our own.' But she couldn't help sending covert little glances in the direction of his beautiful companion. She was obviously Italian, rich and dressed to kill.

'You're not listening to a thing I'm saying . . .'

Quickly she dragged her attention back to her own table, though not quickly enough to avoid catching Paolo's interest. Had he noticed her staring? Watching his dark, lean hands dealing deftly with a soft white roll?

'I said, those are the fishermen's boats.' She turned to where Julian was pointing to a flotilla of craft out on the dusky water. Lights were coming on around the lake—a magic world surrounded by the dark majesty of the duskier mountains. 'They always go out at sunset. In fact, that fish you've ordered was probably caught by one of those very boats last night.'

It had sounded good, too, and was good, she discovered when it came, a local fish marinated with bay leaves. But she was too conscious of Paolo and his companion sitting at that other table to appreciate the meal fully. Sometimes she caught the woman's high, feminine laughter, echoed by the deeper, more resonant sound of his.

The woman was obviously totally absorbed in his company, she thought waspishly, hesitant to admit what an amusing and interesting dinner companion he could be, and yet every time she looked their way he seemed to be looking straight back, until some time during the evening she glanced unwittingly in their direction to realise that they had gone.

She breathed a sigh of relief, glad to be able to relax at last, until a waiter who had crossed to their table announced, 'I have a message from Signor Rossetti, *signore— signorina*. He would like very much for you both to join him for coffee inside.'

And that was how they found themselves in the superlative luxury of the lounge.

Gilt and marble and tuscan columns provided an air of pure majesty, the scattering of easy chairs and tables lending a relaxed ambience to the otherwise palatial decor. In a corner, by the long Venetian windows that were thrown open to the night, a trio played its easy music for the couples who had taken to the floor.

'Chelsea...' That Latin voice washed over her like a warm caress as Paolo pulled out her chair for her and then briefly introduced his beautiful companion.

'I understand you are staying with Paolo. How nice.' The woman whom he'd introduced as Elena Lisi spoke with an accent that was thick and sultry, but the gleam of gold against the shoulder-length hair and at her throat above the exquisitely cut dress was far more genuine, Chelsea couldn't help thinking, than her smile. 'You are staying in his house and he allows you to wear anything but a Rossetti?' Beautiful almond eyes raked over Chelsea's simple black strapless cocktail dress.

'I don't think Chelsea would wear any garment that bore my company's label, Elena.'

Which was putting it a better way than saying she wouldn't be seen dead in one! Chelsea thought, smiling sweetly at Paolo's mockingly amused response. And, trying not to let that raw sexuality unsettle her, she purred, 'Smack on. But then you always are.'

'*Chelsea!*' It was a low hiss through Julian's gritted teeth.

'You cannot say that,' she heard Elena breathe disbelievingly.

Chelsea gave a casual little shrug. 'I just did.' Paolo's gaze was so intense that it was a struggle keeping hers steady. 'There's just too much pretentiousness attached to designer labels,' she couldn't stop herself saying, nevertheless, and paused as a waiter appeared with their coffee and petit fours and moved discreetly away.

She never could help speaking her mind. 'Sometimes,' she said, taking one of the sweetmeats from the plate Paolo was offering her, 'I think some of the smaller designers have as much flair as their more prestigious contemporaries, but because of their lack of resources or contacts— or whatever—their talents go unnoticed.'

She bit into the soft green marzipan, feeling Paolo's gaze resting disconcertingly on her mouth, and she flushed, made to feel as though she had just done something outrageously suggestive.

'I know it's a personal thing—and I'm very aware that I'm at the wrong table to be saying this,' she went on, feeling her lips trembling. Damn the man! she thought. 'But to me it's scandalous to pay a fortune—and I mean *a fortune* for something that might only be worn once and then discarded, simply because it happens to carry the right name on the back of the collar.'

Beneath the table she felt Julian's warning prod. Elena was looking aghast. Surprisingly, though, there was humour in Paolo's raised eyebrows.

'If I were on the other side of the fence I'd probably say I couldn't agree more.'

He was agreeing with her?

'Paolo!' Clearly it wasn't the response that Elena had been expecting either.

'Then why do you do it?' Chelsea asked contentiously.

'He is not the designer,' Elena put in. 'Others do that. He is, however, if you are not aware, the top voice, the king, the most important man of the entire company.'

He shrugged, ignoring Elena's bombastic description of him. 'Family tradition. There is a demand and my company provides it,' he said.

'But you don't agree with it.' Chelsea's hair touched her shoulder as she tilted her head, her expression challenging. 'Isn't that rather hypocritical?'

'*Chel*sea...!' From beside her she caught Julian's embarrassed whisper.

'No.' A dark; lean hand lifted. 'Let her have her views. It's healthy.'

'Thanks,' she said, hating Paolo's patronising tone, hating his relaxed charm, his confidence, that ruthless confidence that could break anyone—as he had broken Neil. 'We even have the vote now back home!'

'She isn't really so militant.' Above the trio's soft music, Julian was attempting to make amends. 'But if she gets a bee in her bonnet...'

Paolo wasn't even looking at him. His glittering gaze was fixed almost mockingly on Chelsea as she raced on, 'I also happen to practice what I preach. In a world where there's so much want it seems grossly obscene to spend so much on something that, after all, is simply a means of keeping oneself warm—or decent. So unfair...'

'Life is unfair.'

'But thousands of pounds for a dress...a *bikini*?' That's the price she had noticed for one in one chic shop in Milan. 'Honestly!'

'One bikini isn't going to save the world,' he said quietly. There was a kind of puzzled assessment about his frown.

'Well, you would say that, wouldn't you?' He had all that wealth because of it, didn't he? she thought, noticing the way his lips compressed with some inner restraint. What other answer could he give? 'It could go some way to helping. Buying food, vital medical aid...'

Now that hard mouth quirked into a rather disbelieving smile. 'That's a surprisingly...I think the phrase is...altruistic view.'

'No, it isn't—it's just practical.'

'Very well.' He made a gallant gesture with his head. 'Nevertheless, I don't believe you're actually doing so badly out of my...''hypocrisy'', as you call it.'

The conversation was just between the two of them. Her dislike of him made her far too voluble, actually gave her a strange sort of buzz out of arguing with him, but now she clammed up, as she felt sure he'd intended her to, her cheeks reddening from that last remark.

One of those awkward little coughs drew her attention back to her fiancé, though she was aware of Paolo's gaze still tugging over her with a hard amusement.

She'd forgotten about Julian, she realised guiltily, and Elena, who had obviously read more than there was into that heated exchange between her and Paolo, she thought, silently abhorring the idea that anyone should think she might actually fancy the man. But Elena did, she realised, seeing how those lovely eyes had narrowed into dark, calculating slits.

'If you do not approve of...exclusivity...' The woman looked at Paolo for assurance that she had the correct word. He neither confirmed nor denied it. 'If you do not mind buying clothes like everybody else, what would you do if you attended a party and saw another woman wearing exactly the same dress?' The horror in Elena's voice said that, for her, it would be a fate worse than death.

Chelsea shrugged. 'I don't know. Probably go up and compliment her on her taste, I suppose.'

Elena looked dumbstruck. She couldn't see Julian's expression because she wasn't looking his way. There was, however, a strange sort of smile on Paolo's lips.

'I'm sure, if she looked like you, the compliment would be well deserved,' he said with mock gallantry; there was a rather bored note in his voice now that told her he wanted to be done with this open warfare with her—at least while the others were around.

'You're too kind,' she said with equally feigned sweetness, and let it go.

Then, surprisingly, Julian was urging her to her feet, towards the dancers on the other side of the room.

'What the hell are you trying to do?' he demanded, coolly furious as he pulled her into the swaying rhythm. 'Lose me the best client I'm ever likely to have? I thought you'd at least try to make an effort, but tonight you weren't just unfriendly you were downright rude to him.'

'What am I supposed to do?' She shot up at him. 'Lick his boots like you constantly appear to be doing?' She couldn't understand Julian. He'd used not to be like this. Such a groveller... 'I'm not impressed by his name or his money, the way you are! The man's detestable...'

'He's also extremely powerful,' Julian reminded her harshly, turning her automatically in his arms. 'And having the sense to recognise that fact isn't licking his boots. One word out of place and you could destroy everything I've worked for.' He glanced worriedly back across the room.

Probably imagining that the man had bionic hearing! she thought peevishly.

'I know he's ruthless. God! I'm not blind to it. But then neither am I stupid. I know which side my bread's buttered, but I want some of the jam as well. Like it or not, sweetheart, he's where the money is, and I'm sure as hell not letting you louse up this one chance to invest in some good, sound insurance for us for the future.'

The vehemence of his speech surprised her. 'What do you mean?' she queried, frowning. The music, though, had come to an abrupt end, and rather ungraciously he released her.

'Let's get back,' he said, with a toss of his chin towards Paolo's table.

'Why? Because he'll cut you off his payroll if he sees you enjoying yourself?' she retorted heatedly, losing patience with Julian's failure to see anything beyond upsetting Paolo. 'You go ahead,' she couldn't help snapping aggravatedly. 'I'd sooner go and have a conversation with the powder-room mirror!'

For a moment, watching him stalk sulkily off, she wondered if she was being too unreasonable, but then, with an exasperated little sigh, she turned and wandered out onto the terrace.

The lamps spilled their soft light across the flagstones; the last of the diners were still sitting there, their conversations muted and relaxed against the strains of the music coming from inside.

What was happening between her and Julian? She tried to analyse it, unhappily making her way across to a secluded corner of the terrace. They didn't even seem to be on the same plane any more. He used to be fun, and yet now the only thing that seemed important to him was getting ahead—not that he hadn't always been ambitious. But he seemed . . . obsessed almost nowadays—obsessed with making money.

'Nursing some guilty secret, Chelsea?'

The deep Latin voice had her swinging round, her heart racing with absurd momentum in finding herself alone with the one person she had come out here to escape.

She laughed—a small trembling sound on the night air. 'Oh, I don't have any of those, Paolo,' she assured him, guessing from his smile that he knew how much she had hoped to avoid him. The very air seemed charged with the dynamism of his presence. 'Do you?'

He laughed low in his throat. 'Guilt or secrets?' His slow strides over the flagstones were almost predatory, dauntingly self-assured.

'Both, but let's try guilt.'

A speculative eyebrow lifted. 'You should know about that.'

'Me?' she uttered innocently, her hand against her breastbone. 'Oh, no.'

'You mean you're conscienceless?'

'Aren't you?'

He smiled, taking in the pale structure of her face, the way the terrace lights played across her soft blonde hair. 'What do you think?'

A sound exploded overhead; a raining shower of sparks appeared from a firework display in the grounds of one of the hotels and for mere seconds, made the sky a mirror of the light-spangled lake.

'I think you're a man who would stop at nothing to get what you wanted.'

For a moment he glanced away as a boat's bell rang out on the night-shrouded water. The dark lines of his profile made her stomach muscles clench almost painfully.

'You obviously know me well.'

'No. Just your type,' she said, her voice oddly husky.

'And what is my type, Chelsea?' He looked—sounded—amused.

'I'll leave that for the Elenas of this world to discover.'

He laughed again—that low, disturbingly sexy laugh. 'You're not intrigued enough to want to find out for yourself?'

Something dark and dangerous tugged at her senses, and a little instinct of self-preservation warned her that she could be getting way out of her depth with him, but resentment drove her on. 'Not interested, is more to the point.'

He muttered something in Italian and, when she frowned, breathed with equally soft vehemence, 'Liar. I would have said, *cara mia*, you were more than just a little...*interested.*'

Her pulse seemed to throb with the rhythm coming now from inside the hotel.

'Spare me, please!' she uttered mirthlessly, his recognition of her shaming attraction to him causing her to turn swiftly away. 'You just aren't funny!'

'Neither is deceit.'

His imperious tone stopped her dead. Or was it the burn of his hand on her arm? Both were too startling for her to be sure.

'Wh-what do you mean?' she faltered.

'I think you know.'

He couldn't...! A pulse worked nervously in her throat. There was no way he could possibly have guessed who she was, surely? she thought, searching for something to say, but, before she could think of something, he went on roughly, 'Much as I share your reluctance to admit knowing Neil Adamson, I do, however, take a very dim view of being lied to.'

Even though she'd thought that he might have guessed, she hadn't seriously expected him to; and his startling reference to her cousin, to her own attempts deliberately to mislead him, caused her to pull forcibly out of his grasp. How long had he known? she wondered hectically. Exactly when had he guessed?

Soft laughter drifted across to them from one of the tables—the easy, romantic sound of a couple in love.

'Did you imagine I wouldn't know everything about everyone I have working for me, Chelsea?' he enquired with a coldly sardonic survey of her startled features. 'At least where my financial affairs are concerned. I must admit I didn't know of Rendell's close association with you when I took him on as one of my advisors, but I did a thorough investigation as soon as I realised he was seriously involved. What a surprise it was to find that he was soon to be betrothed to the little cousin of Neil Adamson—surprise enough to start me wondering. Was it a lucky contact or a coincidence that I should find myself on Rendell's list of clients? And if it was a contact...was there some other motivation besides the financial reward?'

He meant a conspiracy, obviously, although he wasn't actually saying that—some way of paying him back to avenge Neil.

Her cheeks burned scarlet, because wasn't that exactly why she had let him think he was forcing her into coming here, accompanying Julian to his villa—to try somehow to get even with him? She wanted to laugh at herself—at the very dementia of such a notion. She must have been mad, imagining that she could even attempt to outwit this man!

'Do you really think I was happy when Julian told me that you'd become one of his clients?' she threw back at him, glad at least to be able to say exactly what she thought now. 'Do you really imagine that I wanted anything to do with you after what you did to Neil? After you took everything he'd worked for—?' She broke off, swallowing the lump that caught painfully in her throat.

'It's rather ironic, then, isn't it,' he said with that cruel curve to his mouth, 'that you should find yourself so attracted to the man you so thoroughly despise?'

Teeth clenched, blood pounding at his remark, she dug her nails painfully into her palms to stop herself lashing out at him, and, almost as though he could sense how much she ached to, he breathed with intimidating softness, 'I wouldn't if I were you.'

His warning curbed her foolish desire to attack him, restored a little of her poise. Then he said phlegmatically, 'Neil Adamson was a fool.'

'Why?' The look she shot him was hateful, bitter. 'For falling in love with a woman you thought he had no right to be involved with?'

Those dark brows drew together. Evidently he didn't like being reminded. 'Is that your view of it?' There was a hard, abrasive edge to his voice.

'What were you—jealous, Paolo?' Now it was her turn to taunt him, her sultry mouth derisive, her voice unwittingly seductive even in its condemnation of him. 'Was that why you wanted to destroy him? Because you couldn't take someone actually preferring him to you?'

She was only guessing, but she wanted to hit him where it hurt most—at the heart of his masculine ego. If she had succeeded, though, he gave no indication of it. His mouth merely hardened momentarily, although there was an inscrutable query in his eyes.

'He was a careless businessman who refused to see the way the market was going.'

Wings of colour touched her cheeks.

'And so was easy prey for someone like you?'

'Isn't that the way of the world?' He said coldly. 'Survival of the fittest?'

And heaven knew—this man was fit! Chelsea acknowledged resentfully. Fit and hard and as unpitying in his greed for power as a hungry lynx with a stray lamb.

'Your cousin got his priorities mixed up and had to pay for his mistakes,' he stated without any remorse. 'The fact that I was around to take advantage of those...miscalculations...' His wide shoulders lifted, the gesture as casual as the impenitent way in which he had spoken about Neil. 'Someone else would have done it if I hadn't.'

'And that eases your conscience?' she challenged brittly.

Suddenly that hard, handsome face appeared carved out of granite, his one menacing step towards her causing her to shrink back against the cool stonework of the balustrade.

'I don't need an Adamson to offer me any lectures on conscience,' he rasped. 'Particularly one with as little moral integrity as you seem to have.'

Panic leaped in her eyes, her throat going dry because he had bent low towards her and now his hands had come to rest on either side of her on the cool stone, effectively pinning her there.

'I wonder...'

'What?'

He was so close that she hardly dared breathe for fear the action would cause her breasts to touch the gossamer-fine silk of his shirt. She could smell the lethal spice of him—and that was disconcerting enough!

'It took Rendell's brother just a couple of hours to get you up there into his bed that night. Two. Maybe three at the most.' His mouth had twisted with mocking contempt for what he still believed. 'Just how long would it take, I wonder, to get you into mine?'

His voice was silky soft, but she could almost feel the brooding enmity in him—a hatred that seemed to far outweigh the unsavoury little act he thought she had committed.

'I'd die first!' she spat, pushing away one immaculately clad arm. The force she used was unnecessary because, surprisingly, he didn't try to stop her. His soft laughter, however, drifted after her as she fled back across the terrace, mocking her anger, her discomfiture, and that perverse heat that his words had fanned to life deep in her blood.

CHAPTER FOUR

WEARING short pale blue culottes and a white silk camisole, Chelsea made her way downstairs, glad that she and Julian were going to be spending the day away from the villa. She didn't like the way Paolo affected her. It was almost as though her very dislike of him triggered off some warped, self-destructive fascination. Julian's face, however, when she found him in the sunny breakfast room, told its own story, wiping the somewhat forced smile from hers.

'I'm sorry, Chelsea.' She knew, even before he continued, what he was going to say. 'There's been a bit of a crisis. The deal I'm negotiating for Paolo in Como is being threatened by another investor deciding to back out, and I've got to get down there right away and negotiate another possibility on his behalf.'

She had to admit that he looked contrite, but her temper, already frayed by the unsettling time with Paolo the previous night, snapped.

'For heaven's sake, Julian, you promised! You're not being fair!' She knew she sounded like a disgruntled adolescent, but his continuing thoughtlessness on top of her perturbing attraction to the other man was becoming almost too much to bear. 'If we were in Paris—on our honeymoon now—he'd have to have found someone else to handle his precious affairs!'

'But we aren't—and he hasn't. For goodness' sake, Chelsea! How do you think I feel?'

'Stimulated—you always do!'

'That's not true. I was looking forward to coming out with you today—to the two of us being together.'

Had he been? She stared sightlessly at the dark, highly polished wood of the long dresser that housed some of the

68

villa's most exquisite china. She wasn't sure. She just didn't know what to believe any more.

'I'm sorry,' he said then, putting his arms around her. 'I know how much you were looking forward to seeing that villa across the lake. But don't miss out because of me. Paolo's coming down to Como later today as well, and when I told him I was going to persuade you to go ahead without me he said he'd take you—and then bring you down to Como to have lunch with me afterwards.'

'No!' Violently Chelsea pulled out of his arms. 'How could you arrange it?' she said, her mouth twisting in total rejection.

'I didn't. I only mentioned that we'd been planning to go over there—and he came up with the offer out of the blue.'

Chelsea flinched. Somehow she couldn't imagine that there wasn't some ulterior motive behind Paolo's apparently benevolent offer. She couldn't imagine a man like him doing anything without some self-centred purpose.

'And after last night I would have thought the least you'd try and do would be to start co-operating a bit more, making up for nearly costing me one hell of a client . . .'

She cringed, recalling Julian's reaction on the way back to the villa last night when she'd told him that Paolo knew who she was. He'd looked positively apoplectic, and she could hear him now, how fawningly he'd apologised to the man when Paolo had come in only minutes after they had.

'I'm sorry! I never did learn the art of being two-faced!' Grasping one of the high-backed chairs that matched the long, highly polished table, she stared belligerently at the woven tapestry on the far wall that reproduced the reds, greens and golds in the rest of the room. 'You might think he needed apologising to, but personally I think he should be apologising to us after what he did to Neil. Neil was the one who had all he'd worked for stolen from under his very nose!' And worse. There were things that for some reason Neil had only ever told her, that Julian didn't even know about . . .

'Hardly *stolen*,' he emphasised, pulling a face. 'Everything was businesslike and above board. And, contrary to your biased opinion, Neil was no saint.'

'What do you mean?' She couldn't believe that he could actually be taking Paolo's side against her cousin. He never had before. 'Are you saying Neil deserved to lose everything to that mercenary opportunist?'

'Of course not.' He was getting exasperated now. 'For heaven's sake, Chelsea . . .' roughly he pushed a recalcitrant strand of sandy hair back off his forehead '. . . your aversion to the man is almost obsessive. If I didn't know you better I'd think that all your claims to dislike are really a cover-up for something else.'

A wave of disgust—of self-loathing—couldn't fully disguise the throb of tension that pulsed through her. Julian was way, way too near the truth.

'Like what?' she demanded, but Julian was looking distractedly over her shoulder.

She glanced round, realising, with a sinking feeling in her stomach, that Paolo had just entered the room.

Had he heard? If he had, she thought, trying to still her racing heart and ignore Julian's sullen features, he made no comment, and intuitively she knew, as she struggled against the impact of his devastating image in a silver-grey suit, white shirt and silver tie, that, despite his calculated heartlessness, some inherent streak of integrity would prevent him from doing so.

'I believe you're coming with me. Are you ready?'

She wanted to protest, tell him that he could stick his lift, but that cool, authoritative demeanour defied such outlandish behaviour. She hadn't eaten breakfast either, but the thought of spending any length of time with Paolo had totally robbed her of her appetite, and so she hurried off to fetch the blue silk shirt that matched her swinging culottes and, with an almost grudging peck on the cheek from Julian at the bottom of the stairs, followed Paolo reluctantly out to the car.

She had imagined that the journey to the eighteenth-century villa would be unrelaxed, the conversation between her and Paolo strained at the very least. And indeed, had it been left to her, she thought, it might have been, unable as she was to forget her acute dislike for him along with that disquieting remark he had made only hours before about getting her into his bed.

He made no reference to the previous night, however, talking about everything else instead—her job, his, their location—and, when they were on the ferry, pointing out the panoramic views from the middle of the lake, their own villa in the hills behind them, a mountain village worth visiting, the imposing majesty of the peaks and their familiar names. But for a moment when he took her elbow to assist her back into the car before they drove onto dry land again, she had to admit that the crossing had been unexpectedly pleasant.

'You see? We didn't sink,' he laughed, referring to some wry comment that she had made earlier about not wanting to wind up at the bottom of the deepest lake in Europe. 'If we had, you can rest assured that I would not have let you drown.'

Why not? You didn't help Neil when he needed you most, her heart cried bitterly, her brooding brown eyes resting too willingly on him as he drove off the ferry.

His jacket was discarded in the back of the car, and the short-sleeved white shirt he wore contrasted with the hard tan of his arms—arms that were strong and muscled beneath their dark feathering of hair. The subtle gold of his slimline wrist-watch, secured by a black strap, glinted occasionally in the sun.

'I wish I could give you the same assurance,' she quipped, and sensed the subtle movement of an eyebrow. Take it any way you like, she thought.

It wasn't that long before they reached the classical villa, and it wasn't until she was getting out of the car, thanking him for the lift, that she realised he was getting out too.

'I thought you were going somewhere on business...'

He smiled at her unconcealed dismay. 'Unfortunately I am. You don't think I normally dress like this—' his open gesture drew her gaze unwittingly to his chest and the dark shading of hair beneath his shirt '—just to go sightseeing? Not in this heat. However, my appointment isn't until later—in Como. In the meantime...' he sent a glance towards the imposing structure that had once been a nobleman's summer palace—an extravagant sanctuary tailored with magnificent balustrades and statues and breathtaking gardens '...such beauty shouldn't be observed without an escort, so...I'm afraid you've got me with you whether you like it or not.'

Surprisingly, she realised, he wasn't referring solely to the villa. His glittering irises—resting on her now—were, like his voice, dangerously disturbing, and with a quickening pulse she looked away to the splashes of vibrant colour supplied by some exotic shrubs that were growing in the elegant gardens, saying tremulously, 'Be my guest.'

Her reluctance to have him accompanying her, however, was soon dispelled by her interest in the villa's tapestries and paintings, of which Paolo seemed to have surprising knowledge, and in the ornately decorated walls and ceilings and the elaborate eighteenth-century furniture, but the thing that held her attention most was the romantic sculpture of Canova's *Cupid and Psyche*.

They came upon it suddenly and unexpectedly, the sheer grace and potency of its subject causing a funny feeling in her stomach.

'It's passionate, yet tragic.'

Reluctantly, Chelsea drew her gaze from the supine form of the naked girl whose arms were extended, her lips uptilted, to the naked winged god behind her, standing with one hand clasped beneath her breast.

'Tragic?' she queried, frowning.

'All the intensity of loving conveyed and immortalised in the longing for a kiss that will never be fulfilled.' Paolo's voice was as sensual as the sculpture—and more discomfiting as she found herself wondering, with shocked agitation, what it would be like actually to be kissed by him. 'Can you not feel the yearning, Chelsea? The frustration?'

Mentally she tried to blot it out, but the image refused to be denied: her own supine nakedness, her hair wild against a pillow, the hands that burned her flesh dark against the pale sheen of her breast...

No! Suddenly she couldn't stay there any longer, and, ignoring him, she sped away from the overwhelming sensuality of the statue. She came out of the villa, needing the liberating perspective of ordinary things: the glittering blue of the sky, the sound of a child calling in the grounds, the harsh reality of the hot sun on her face and arms.

'Are you always so profoundly embarrassed by anything remotely sexual? I would have said, with your experience, Chelsea, you could take a thing like that in your stride.'

Damn him! He had followed her, she realised, staring down onto the superb landscaping of the garden. At its entrance pillared statues guarded the great gates beyond which the sapphire water glistened, but she barely took any of it in. Her breasts were lifting as rapidly as if she had been denied air.

'You would think that, wouldn't you?' she snapped, hating his acute perception of every small weakness, especially when he went on, ignoring her strong denial.

'If I were Rendell I would have rid you of those inhibitions by now.'

His remark sent a sensual little shiver through her, despite the sun that had prompted her to slip on her top to protect her shoulders.

'Well, you're not! And, as you so accurately pointed out, I don't have any inhibitions,' she retorted, flustered. How had they got onto this subject, anyway?

'Then perhaps it's Rendell.'

'Julian? Inhibited?' Beneath the vivid sun her hair shone like ripe wheat as she tilted her head, laughing humourlessly. 'Why? Just because he respects my wish for separate rooms? I suppose in your book that only makes him half a man.'

'In my book, as you call it,' he said soberly, following her down the balustraded steps into the formal garden, 'the situation would never arise. Neither would leaving my bride at the altar.'

Flabbergasted, Chelsea stopped dead as he caught up with her. 'You hardly gave him a choice!' Her eyes were dancing with incredulity. 'If that spoilt little niece of yours hadn't admitted to slapping that pack of lies at his feet—'

'I could have done nothing,' he said quietly, 'if he had married you first and brought you with him as I half expected he would.'

For a moment his statement rendered her speechless. 'You could have terminated your contract with him—just as you threatened to do when we were still in Milan.'

'Not when I found out the truth—as I would have sooner or later. As I always do, Chelsea.' That hard self-assurance made her shiver. Yes, she could believe that.

'What's so unsettling you about being with me, *mia cara*? Why the continual need to make your hatred for me so obvious? Is it only because of what you think I might have done to your cousin? Or is it the shock of finding yourself so powerfully attracted to his persecutor?'

She darted a sidelong glance at him, her mouth dry, her pulse beating enervatingly fast. 'You're very sure of yourself,' she accused him breathlessly. 'What gives you the right to even suggest that I...?' She couldn't go on, afraid that if she did her voice might betray these ludicrous physical responses to him that she seemed to have so little control over.

'That you what?' he asked. 'That you were hit...right between the eyes, I think is the expression—just as I was that day you stormed into my office. And that despite our differences you're almost desperate to discover the sort of pleasure you know I could give you—a man you profess to hate.'

'No!'

'No?' His smile was hard and cynical. 'That's why you came out of there—' this with a jerk of his chin towards the palace '—like a bolting filly on heat, because you see yourself in the type of embrace with me that for some reason you're determined to deny yourself with Rendell.'

'That's not true!'

She had darted away from him, back through the gardens, past orange-tree pergolas and camellia hedges—their flowers over now, having succumbed to the more vibrant blossoming of other colourful shrubs: cacti, palms and exotic tropical plants that she couldn't even identify, yet which made a lasting statement to some long-dead nobleman's indulgence.

It wasn't until she came round the side of the building to where they had parked the car that she slackened her steps, ashamed to acknowledge even to herself that a lot of what he had said was true. And it came as a shock to realise that he must have chased after her with the speed of Eros, because his hand was on her shoulder, pulling her mercilessly round, and the next minute her protest was being stifled by the hard, determined pressure of his mouth.

Excitement catapulted through her, her hands coming up to clutch his shoulders as he spread his legs on either side of her, forcing her back against the hard, hot bodywork of the car.

There were other people around them. She could hear their distant voices, the slamming of car doors, but she didn't care. She was like a savage being, not inhibited at all, greedily drinking in the potent elixir of his kiss, his scent, the hard warmth of his body, every nerve firing into life. As she had known it would.

The hot metalwork burned through her silk culottes and she whimpered painfully so that he eased her away from it and into him. A man who desired her enough to kiss her openly, in public, she thought headily, feeling like that sensual maiden, who had been unashamed to be seen giving herself to her lover, wanting to be naked like her—naked in this man's arms...

'*No!*' Somehow she found the will to tear her mouth from his, breathing raggedly as she stood slumped against the car, now that he had released her. His eyes, dark and brooding, met the self-disgust that twisted her bruised lips. 'How dare you...?'

She couldn't admit that she was as much to blame, even when her very lack of composure revealed how shattered she had been by his kiss.

'Yes, I dare,' he grated breathlessly, surprisingly as much out of control as she was. 'Because, despite all your claims to outrage, you wanted it as much as I did. And don't start to give me any drivel about being engaged, because we both know how much that means to you, don't we?'

He was unlocking her door, opening it for her, and numbly she climbed into the car, too shamed, stunned by what she had allowed to happen to speak.

Absently, her thumb toyed with the ruby and diamond engagement ring on her finger. How could she? How could she have let him kiss her like that without even trying to stop him?

Staring straight ahead as he pulled out onto the road again, she found it no help at all to tell herself that she had had no choice, that he had been arrogantly determined. If only that were true! So he'd kissed her, but it was the way she had responded to him that was making her feel sick with shame. How could she have been so disloyal to Julian? Perhaps that was understandable, though, given the way he had been treating her lately, she thought, trying to justify her actions. But with a man she hated, whom she had so vehemently condemned at every given opportunity?

'Stop sulking.' It was a soft rebuke across the car's cool, air-conditioned interior. 'It isn't as though we made love back there,' he sneered, just short of irritably, his words not helping, because to make love had been what she had wanted. Even now the memory of his hard mouth on hers, of his crushing strength pressing her against the car sent a sharp contraction down through the heart of her femininity. Oh, yes, for all her remorse and self-loathing, she still wanted to!

'Could you drop me back in the direction of the ferry? I think I'll go back to the villa,' she uttered when they stopped at a junction and she realised that she still had the choice. She didn't think she could stay in this car with him all the way to Como, let alone face Julian. She needed to think. To get her senses back on an even keel. To try and sort herself out.

'Don't be silly.' As she made to open her door he slammed on the central-locking system. 'Stay here,' he commanded, looking back at the road.

Tight-lipped, defiantly Chelsea released the little black button beneath her window. 'I can't,' she objected, finding her further attempt to get out thwarted when he reached across and pulled her door closed. She shrank back into her seat, fighting the betraying frisson that ran through her from contact with that warm arm.

'You can and you will,' he stated as the sports car's thrust of power pushed her deeper into her seat. 'Playing the guilt-stricken lover doesn't become you, *cara*. And imagine what Rendell will think if he finds out you've come with me this morning and then don't turn up to have lunch with him as previously arranged. Don't you think he might suspect something if you keep up this continual vendetta with me, Chelsea?' For a moment only the fierce growl of the car intruded on the silence, and then Paolo murmured, 'If he doesn't already.'

'What do you mean?' she challenged him warily, although she knew. He'd overheard exactly what Julian had been saying to her that morning. Pride, though, wouldn't let her openly acknowledge it, or the fact that she was so disillusioned with her engagement that she didn't know what she thought or felt any more, and quickly she added, 'There's nothing to suspect.'

He sent a glance her way, the slide of his gaze down her slender body making her pulses race, her breasts flower in traitorous mockery beneath her silky camisole. Out of the corner of her eye she saw his mouth twitch with something like self-satisfaction before he turned his attention back to the road again, not needing to say anything.

Their journey continued in silence then, for which Chelsea was grateful. She didn't want to talk to him and sat silently nursing the confused turmoil of her emotions as the road wound alongside the sparkling waters of the lake.

Steep hillsides rose sharply on her side of the car, green-wooded terrain stretching away to the odd mountain village, the site of an ancient church, or simply to the more barren, majestic peaks. The pale, terracotta-roofed buildings of a small port stood serenely in the sun, and somewhere in the distance the vineyards of some once stately villa gave onto a sweep of olive groves, undulating like a grey-green sea. The colourful canvasses of a campsite caught her eye, and somewhere on the journey they passed a funicular railway, alive with tourists on their way up or back from viewing some scenic point.

'Do you ski?'

'*What?*' His startling question jolted her attention back to his side of the car and the figure skimming behind one of the shimmering boats out on the lake. Of course. He meant water-ski. 'Y-yes, I've done a bit in the past,' she answered falteringly, wondering if he'd sensed anything strange in her initial reaction, although he didn't comment upon it.

'Perhaps I'll take you out some time,' he said.

What did he mean—her and Julian, or just her? she wondered, her heart leaping absurdly, and didn't need to answer because the traffic that had been gradually slowing down in front had now ground to a complete halt and all Paolo's attention was on something a little way ahead.

Anyway, what could she have said? That after today she would make sure never to be alone with him again? She was much too vulnerable at the moment, too mixed up emotionally. And as Paolo obviously thought the worst about her—and justifiably now, she realised, still mortified by her abandoned response to his kiss—he clearly wouldn't

have any qualms about trying to seduce her. And if he did...
She sucked in a breath, cringing from the truth as if it was
a dark tormentor. She wasn't sure that she would have the
defences needed to resist.

The dull click of the central-locking system preceded his
soft curse in Italian. He had cut the engine and was trying
to get out—as other people in the car in front had, she
realised, aware then that his door kept relocking itself in
spite of his attempts to release the button manually. 'You
realise you're responsible for this,' he accused her surprisingly, still making every attempt to get out.

'Me?' Chelsea breathed, flabbergasted, wondering why
he sounded so annoyed. How could she possibly have had
anything to do with messing up the electrics of his car?

His savage expletive as he managed finally to fling his
door open before the button could snap again was something quite crude, she was sure. Perhaps she'd done something when she'd unlocked her side earlier, she thought.
Even so, that was hardly any reason for him to react so
harshly...

More peeved than anything else by his attitude, she successfully managed to follow his example and get out of the
car. After the vehicle's cool interior, the temperature hit
her like a wall of heat.

She would stretch her legs—let him cool off for a bit. Or
his temper at least! she thought wryly, because already she
could feel the intensity of the sun penetrating her fine top
as she inhaled the lakeland breeze, wondering if Paolo's
mood stemmed from her obvious remorse after that kiss.
He'd been talking to her reasonably enough just prior to
that.

Further along the road she could see now that a truck
had shed some of its load. The driver looked harassed, but,
judging from the number of helpers who were passing up
the dusty crates to him, it wouldn't take too long to reload
it. She was just coming round the bonnet to get a better
view of the lake when a stray glance in Paolo's direction
stopped her in her tracks.

He was standing, head lowered, with his fingers splayed on the car roof, breathing deeply.

'Are . . . are you all right?' She stopped short of placing her hand on that tanned, muscular arm. Tension had harshened his features and there was a dewy dampness beneath the sprinkling of grey at his temples.

He didn't respond for a moment, appearing to hold his breath, and the face he finally turned towards her was devoid of any emotion.

'Would it somehow please you to think that I wasn't?'

There was nothing wrong with him. She had imagined it, she thought, when the mocking cynicism of his tone made her wish she hadn't asked.

'Of course it wouldn't,' she said, oddly stung that he might think so. 'I wouldn't like to see anyone suffer—even if I didn't like them,' she was unable to prevent herself tagging on.

'In that case—' he smiled now, putting his key in the lock, holding it there while the car's sophisticated computer system surprisingly corrected the fault '—it's a pity I am never sick. It might be worth it just to have you soothe my fevered brow.' But his laughter was sardonic as he tried his door once more to make sure it was working properly, and, feeling foolish, Chelsea swept away from him to her own side of the car, wishing that she hadn't been stupid enough to show him any compassion.

Over the next few days she tried to avoid him, which was difficult, especially at mealtimes, although, to her relief, the business in Como seemed to be nearing completion, which meant that Julian was around more now. That, however, brought its own problems, forcing her to reassess their relationship, accept the fact that things just weren't the same. And they came to a head, startlingly and unexpectedly, one afternoon when they were sunbathing and Julian suddenly asked, 'When are we going to set another date, Chelsea?'

Lazing on the raft which they had swum out to earlier from the private shingle beach beyond the villa's steeply rambling garden, her fiancé's question acted like a pin on the small bubble of serenity that she'd managed briefly to capture.

'Let's not think about it yet.' She was lying with her eyes still closed, her face turned to the sun, letting its warmth soothe and relax her. Paolo had gone out for the day and she was enjoying the brief respite from his disturbing influence on her senses, trying not to think about it—about anything. 'Let's just enjoy the moment,' she murmured.

'Don't you trust me?'

'Why shouldn't I trust you?' she laughed, with slightly more affectation than sincerity.

'Then why keep putting it off, changing the subject whenever I bring it up?'

'I don't,' she contended, squinting as she opened her eyes and saw him supported by an elbow, looking down at her. He had mentioned it when they had been looking around Como earlier in the week. Then, though, she'd been nursing a bitter remorse over what had happened between her and Paolo that morning before he'd driven her down there. Confusion had followed as she'd realised that it stemmed more from the knowledge that she could even want a man like Paolo than from any disloyalty to Julian.

'Do you still want to marry me?' Julian asked broodily.

Did she? The question was a subtle intrusion on her thoughts, like the familiar sound of the hydrofoil that she could hear making its progress further down the lake.

'I'm here with you, aren't I?' she parried.

'In body,' he muttered, the unwelcome hand suddenly running over her soft curves making her tense rigid.

His sun-bleached hair, falling forward, became a blur as he took her mouth with his, but the excitement that had once been there refused to surface, swamped by the memory of that other kiss at that other villa—of Paolo's determination as he'd forced her back against his car.

Hating herself—confused—she broke Julian's kiss, turning her head away.

'See what I mean?' he grumbled, sitting up.

'I'm just not in the mood,' she breathed, bringing herself upright, her expression troubled, because the problem was more than just her mood. It wasn't just Paolo... 'Anyway, people can see,' she said, attempting an excuse.

'What *people*?' Julian scoffed in his frustration, and, looking around, she could see why. The trees that crowded almost onto the beach shrouded them from the villa, even out here. Only the occupants of a sailing boat, drifting on the sapphire water half a mile away, could see them—and they'd have to use binoculars. 'I know you've got this crazy notion about wanting to wait—and I've always respected that—but you're never in the mood these days,' he complained, looking totally disgruntled.

Chelsea fell back onto the raft, listening to the gentle lapping of the water around it. Absently, her gaze traced the progress of some graceful water-bird into the brilliant blue, following it until it was lost against the hazy backdrop of the mountains.

'What do you expect?' she murmured, scarcely able to keep the disillusionment out of her voice.

'I expect you...' he flopped down beside her again, his hand supporting his head '...simply to understand. Life's bound to be tough for a bit, while I'm trying to make some money. But we'll be able to enjoy something like this...' his free arm embraced the idyllic setting and the rambling grounds of the villa above them '...for ourselves one day.'

'You think so?' She couldn't help sounding sceptical. 'Fat lot of good that will be if you're always working,' she said, closing her eyes. She didn't want to think about the future—idealised or otherwise.

'Do you think I intend to be?' Julian gave a cynical snort. 'I intend to enjoy myself before I'm old and decrepit. Why should I sit back and watch people like Paolo have all the fun?'

'Because he's in a different league to you—and always will be,' Chelsea decided to remind him. 'And what do you intend to do if you aren't out there earning it?' she said wearily, bored with the subject.

'Don't you call bowing down to all that power and authority earning it?' he said, with a resentment that surprised her. 'There are other ways—other means . . .'

Through the stillness of the afternoon another bird cawed above them. 'What do you mean?' Raising herself up on her elbows, Chelsea frowned across at him, his words only just sinking in.

'I mean he's got millions. Houses. That car. A boat.' He was looking past her, towards the sleekly aggressive power-craft that they could see inside the purpose-built structure on the shingle, and there was a petulant thrust to his lower lip. 'He's got so much it's obscene.'

'But he works hard for it. You've said so yourself often enough.'

She didn't like defending Paolo, but neither had she ever begrudged anyone who worked hard having more than she did, and she started at Julian's explosive, 'So do I! And if being his advisor doesn't pave the way for opportunity . . .'

'What opportunity? What are you talking about? Has he offered you something, some other position?' She was sitting up fully now, glancing distractedly towards the mountains above where thick, fluffy clouds were starting to gather. Vaguely she recalled Paolo saying earlier that the evening promised rain.

'Oh, for heaven's sake—use your initiative, Chelsea!' And more rudely he went on, 'Thank goodness it's mine we're relying on to make our fortune, not yours! I'm negotiating on his behalf all the time, aren't I? And so much of his money goes through my hands. Where do you think all those paintings in the flat, the fully paid-up car, that holiday last autumn in Mauritius came from?'

Chelsea stared at him. She couldn't believe what she was hearing.

'I thought...' What had she thought? That those oils had come within the budget of his already enviable salary. That he was buying the car over a period—monthly, like everybody else. 'I paid my way.' Stunned, numb, it was all she could think of to say in response to his reference to their holiday. It had been expensive and she had saved hard, insisted on paying her share unless he'd forcefully insisted otherwise—like with that upgraded air ticket...

'You paid what I asked you for. We couldn't have done all the things we did—gone everywhere, drunk the *best* champagne,' he emphasised roughly, 'even on my salary, let alone on yours.'

'I didn't know we were drinking the best champagne!' It seemed a ludicrous statement to make after the things he had just been saying, but he had been secretive about a lot of things during that holiday—or rather, dishonest. It was a shock to have to bring herself to realise that now.

'You mean...you're...lying about negotiations? Falsifying documents...?' Her head was in a spin. 'That's *fraud*,' she murmured, horrified, her voice barely audible.

Julian blew down his nose. 'Reaping proper rewards is more appropriate,' he returned with a grimace. 'Anyway, he can afford it. Hey! Where are you going?'

As she made to slip off the raft, his hand was on her arm.

'I've heard enough!' she choked back. 'Let me go!'

But he didn't. The raft bobbed violently as he raised himself up on his haunches, held her there still struggling against him.

'You wanted to get even with him, didn't you?' he reminded her. And roughly he added, 'Remember Neil?'

'But not this way!' she spat out, repelled by what Julian was doing.

'What better way is there?' His whole tone, his expression was incredulous. And suddenly, with his nails digging into her flesh, he ground out, 'You aren't going to tell him, are you?' The notion that she might do so contorted his features with a hard aggression that she'd never seen in him before.

'Hardly,' she breathed, pulling free at last, and, plunging into the warm water, she struck out for the shingle. If Julian wanted to play a dangerous game with Paolo's money...

She couldn't think, couldn't bear even to imagine the consequences of what would happen if he was caught. Paolo wouldn't take it lying down! She knew from the way he had dealt with her cousin—who had only dared try to take a woman from him—how merciless he could be if he was crossed. But that Julian could be so deceitful, do something so *stupid*...

Her heart aching with desolation, she knew that she could never marry him now. Yet, strangely, she couldn't even weep about that as she ran, wet and sickened, up through the grounds and to the house.

Slamming into her room, she refused to answer when Julian banged on her door, needing time to calm down, digest everything he had disclosed to her before she could face him again. And when, having showered and changed, she went downstairs with the intention of trying to make him see sense, realise the seriousness of what he was doing, it was to find only Maria, who told her that Signor Rendell had asked her to pass on the message that Signor Rossetti had telephoned, that he was driving down to Como with some papers Signor Rossetti needed, and that neither of them were expected to be back for dinner.

Thanking her, Chelsea ordered some sandwiches for herself to be sent up to her room, most of which she left, the awful things she'd learned about Julian that afternoon robbing her of any desire to eat.

She went to bed at some ridiculously early hour, and then found it impossible to sleep. Some time around midnight she heard them drive in—the unmistakable diesel engine of the hired car, the throaty growl of Paolo's Ferrari—and a little time afterwards Julian came up and knocked on her door, called softly to her, but she pretended to be asleep.

She didn't want to speak to him, wouldn't have known what to say even if she had. While she had been lying there, though, she had come to a decision, and swiftly now she pushed back the covers and stole quietly out of bed.

If Julian was doing something dishonest, criminal . . . even the thought of it made her breath catch in her lungs . . . then she didn't want to stick around and look as though she were in any way involved. She had to leave—now.

Starting to gather a few of her possessions together, she decided that it would be senseless trying to make a hasty departure with everything she had brought. Paolo could send her case on, and if he thought it strange that she should leave without a word during the night—well, Julian would just have to think up some plausible reason to offer him. That was his problem—not hers!

Within ten minutes she was ready. Armed with only a thin cotton jacket and an overnight bag, she crept down through the sleeping villa without switching on a light and made her way quietly outside, praying that she wouldn't alarm the dogs. They knew her, of course. She had seen the three Dobermann pinschers often enough with Riccardo, their handler, even if he hadn't let her pet them. Even so, she didn't want to start them barking and rouse the whole house.

There was no moon, and the clouds that had been building up over the mountains that afternoon had resulted in several hard showers earlier. Even now she felt the cool splash of raindrops touch her face so she slipped her arms into her jacket, making her way down through the pitch-blackness of the trees that bordered the drive until she came up against the shadowy stone of the high wall.

The gates would be locked, so there would be no use attempting to leave by the conventional method, but one thing she had always been good at was climbing trees.

Swiftly she reached for an overhanging branch that she could just make out growing near the wall and started to pull herself up, then gave a startled cry as it suddenly snapped, and she landed, hard and awkwardly, on the wet grass.

'*Oh, no.*' It was starting to rain heavily now and she winced from the sharp pain in her right knee as she got up, but that was the least of her worries.

Above the patter of the rain on the leaves, a chillingly deep bark sounded somewhere in the grounds. Then another, and another, until the barking became a frenzied, raucous chorus.

CHAPTER FIVE

THE security lights had come on around the villa and the barking was growing fiercer, closing in on her as she grabbed the bag which she had dropped and threw herself determinedly at the trunk of the tree.

She was wet now, and her knee was hurting, but that was preferable to staying there and facing any awkward questions. Besides, the dogs' savage barking was terrifying, making her blood run cold.

As she clung to the rough trunk like a mad thing, determined to get a firm foothold, one of the dog's jaws clamped aggressively onto her jeans just above her ankle. She heard the denim tear, felt the animal's warm saliva on her skin.

'Get away from me!' Frantically she tried to shake it off, but the creature was too well trained, and the next minute she was being tugged, frightened and screaming, to the ground.

'Help me! Somebody help me!' The dog had her now by the sleeve of her jacket while the others were running round her, their snarls making her sick with fear. Petrified, she could feel their hot breath on her face, see the fierce clamp of vicious white teeth bared to sink in—to devour...

'No!'

'Demonio! Bruno! Lupo!' Several deep masculine shouts made her captor instantly release her, another sending the dogs bounding off in total obedience to the command.

'What the...?' Hard hands were hauling her unceremoniously to her feet. 'Chelsea?' Harsh puzzlement was lining Paolo's familiar features. 'What are you doing out here? What's going on?'

From the way his partially buttoned shirt was stuffed loosely into his waistband he had obviously been dragged out of bed by the commotion, and Chelsea swallowed. Whatever could she say?

'N-nothing's going on . . .' She put her hand to her head, her bones feeling like jelly from that brutal canine assault.

'Are you hurt?' he demanded as she gasped from the pain that shot through her knee. He was looking thoroughly mystified as well as concerned.

'If I were it would be no thanks to you,' she breathed, pulling out of his grasp, rubbing her arm where the dog's teeth had bruised her flesh. 'God! They're vicious.'

'What do you expect? You should have more sense than to be prowling around out here in the early hours. What were you doing out here anyway?'

Chelsea searched for some plausible reason to offer him but not before those keen eyes had taken in the broken branch and the overnight bag lying on the ground, and she saw the puzzlement deepen on his face. 'Thinking of leaving?' There was a less than friendly emotion behind his smile.

'What does it look like?' She sounded braver than she felt, but then she could scarcely try and fool him that she was out here for the good of her health, could she? she thought, hoping that he'd think her voice shook solely because of her encounter with his dogs.

'In this?' His chin jerked upwards, his expression saying it all—that even without the rain that was really coming down now it took some believing. 'In the middle of the night?'

Scepticism coloured his voice, and Chelsea caught her breath. If she were in his shoes she'd think it pretty strange as well.

'What were you doing? Planning to meet some secret lover? Or is Rendell with you?'

'No! Of course not.' She said it quickly—much too quickly, she realised, seeing the line deepening between those penetrating eyes. Why would he think that? 'We had a row—all right?' she breathed, the burden of Julian's guilt weighing her down, making her nerves tremble beneath Paolo's dark suspicion.

'So why not leave tomorrow? You're hardly sharing his bed.' And when she didn't respond immediately—couldn't, because she didn't have a clue how to without telling him the truth—he said firmly, stooping to retrieve her bag, 'I think you had better come back inside.'

Chelsea felt her throat constrict. What further explanation could she give him? she wondered, shrugging off the strong hand at her elbow, finding that it took all her physical endurance to do more than simply hobble now because of the pain in her knee, although she was determined not to show any weakness in front of him.

Riccardo came up to them and said something to him in Italian. He had the dogs under control now. Three sets of ferocious teeth seemed to be grinning at her, pleased with their night's work.

'*Si.*' Paolo's voice was low as he darted a glance up at the house and dismissed the security man. Then at the door he gave an order to Maria, who was standing there in her dressing gown. She directed a baffled glance towards Chelsea and immediately scurried away.

'In here.' She felt like a criminal as Paolo indicated for her to precede him into the lounge. The light he snapped on illuminated the recesses and the carved pillars, the overall opulence of the elegant room.

Obeying him, Chelsea subsided gratefully onto the rich brocade of the settee. The walk hadn't done her knee any good at all and the pain was causing her eyes to burn with smarting tears.

'Crying?' Those hawk-like eyes didn't miss anything as he turned from tossing her overnight bag onto one of the tastefully carved chairs. 'Was the fight with your boyfriend that painful?'

'That's personal,' she retorted, recoiling from the obvious cynicism in his voice, her eyes trained on the graceful sculpture of a water-carrier—one of a pair that were recessed on either side of the door. 'And I'm not crying.'

'So what was it about?'

Chelsea glanced down at the mosaic marble of the floor. 'That's hardly your concern.'

'It is when one of my guests nearly gets herself ripped apart by my dogs. So...' He moved towards her, the fine quality of his shirt revealing the dark, lean power of him beneath and the darker body hair that curled crisply above the open neck. 'You had a fight.'

'Yes!' She looked rebelliously up at him now. 'Let's just leave it like that, can we?'

Those powerful shoulders shrugged. 'I would. But I cannot believe you're the type who simply runs away. We also both know your propensity for telling the truth isn't all it should be, don't we?'

His voice was silkily intimidating, and unconsciously Chelsea moistened her lips. 'What are you implying?' she whispered, the sudden pounding of her heart bringing heightened colour to her cheeks. A droplet of rain ran down her neck and she shuddered, though she was far from cold.

'Is there anything to imply?' His smile was a tight, emotionless movement of lips. 'I simply find it...what is the word?...bizarre, *mia cara*, that a fight with Rendell should prompt you to take such drastic steps—especially when I see you're still wearing his ring.'

Only because she hadn't taken it off yet, because she was too shaken still by Julian's crime to consider anything but getting away from here, from a man who, she had no doubt, would be totally merciless if he found out what Julian had done. 'I'm also not oblivious to the fact that you would like to get your...claws into me in any way you could.'

His loathing was a palpable thing, and a little shiver of fear played along Chelsea's spine.

'What, by making off with the silver?' She made an effort to laugh, the highly strung little sound giving her away. This was ludicrous! It was Julian who was committing the crime against him, not her, and yet here he was thinking that she...That she what? She didn't know. 'Do you really think you're so important to me that I'd—'

Another step brought him closer. 'That you'd what, Chelsea?'

She swallowed, shivering as another droplet ran down her neck. Her hair was soaked, so was his—but he didn't look the wet, bedraggled mess that she was sure the night had made of her.

'That I'd...' she took a breath, and, feeling braver—remembering Neil '...take anything from you even if I was paid!'

His mouth was coldly sardonic. 'Why not? Your cousin wasn't so reluctant.'

His hatred for Neil speared her. What he was talking about was the rivalry of two men for one woman. 'People are different!'

'Are they? There are many different ways of taking, Chelsea.' His eyes were glittering with a hatred so intense that she felt it like a furnace threatening to consume her. 'So what were you planning to do—live a life of self-deluded innocence while enjoying the benefits of your fiancé's ill-gotten gains?'

'I haven't—' Taken anything from you, she was about to fling at him again. Instead she stared up at him with trembling lips parted, her eyes wide with a dark, bewildered fear. 'Wh-what do you mean?' she whispered, the sound coming out like a guilty little croak.

'You know very well.'

Yes, she did. Her mind reeled. But how did he?

Involuntarily her tongue strayed across her suddenly dry lips. 'You—you know?' It was a timid sound, born out of pure shock—three trembling words which, she realised desolately now, had just innocently and unintentionally betrayed Julian.

'Yes,' he breathed, with an intimidating softness. 'What did you imagine, *cara*? That I was some sort of halfwit? That I would be totally unaware of what was going on?'

There was a faint-hearted knock at the door and Maria popped her head round. She handed Paolo a towel and, clearly aware of the mood that her employer was in, quickly retreated.

'Here.' He flung the towel at Chelsea with a vehemence that said he would have preferred to beat her with it.

Numbly she picked it up, pressing it to the soggy blonde strands at the nape of her neck.

'When—when did you find out?' She couldn't believe it. She hadn't known herself until that afternoon.

He hooked his thumbs into the waistband of his trousers, standing there despising and ruthlessly judging her.

'For certain, just a couple of days ago—but I've suspected something for a long time. Why do you think I asked you both here? Certainly not to offer my repentance for the impediment of your precious wedding plans! I wanted Julian where I could keep both eyes on him while my legal people were finishing their...investigative work. How much satisfaction has it given you, I wonder, knowing that every penny he put into your bank account was being illegally financed by mine?'

The hard contours of his face were savage, and quickly Chelsea breathed, 'It wasn't like that!' It sounded like a desperate plea by the guilty, but she had to make him believe her. 'I didn't know. Not until today. That's why I was leaving. I was appalled—frightened. I didn't want to be involved in anything Julian was doing wrong.'

'Hah!' His disbelieving bark of laughter made her flinch. He swore viciously in his own language, his calculating survey of her contorting his features into something that made fear as she knew it only a tepid thing compared with the shuddering trepidation that he was stirring in her now. 'You would even turn him in—the man you profess to love— to get yourself...' he gave the briefest pause while he sought the right expression '...off the hook?' The condemnation in his face, his voice, told her what he thought of that.

'I wouldn't! I didn't know. Paolo—you've got to believe me!'

'Why?'

'Because it's the truth.'

He laughed again—a cold, contemptuous sound. To him her claims to truth meant nothing, and she couldn't blame him. Not when she had lied in the beginning.

'We both know how much reliance we can place on that! I believe you'd lie and cheat and deceive your way into the record books without a prick of conscience if you thought it would get what you wanted. I know, remember? You weren't showing much trace of virtue that night in that hotel room with his brother!'

So it all came back to that. Roughly she thumped the towel down beside her. 'That wasn't what it seemed!'

'Wasn't it?'

'No! For heaven's sake, Paolo!' She met his gaze now with indignation burning in hers. 'There wasn't anything in that! You only believed what you wanted to believe—'

'What I saw with my own eyes.' And at that moment they were glittering with disgust. 'Heard!'

'You just thought you saw something because I wanted you to think it,' she explained, because it was imperative now that he believe her. 'But I only went up there with Murray because he'd asked me to help him wrap up the earrings and necklace he'd bought Christine for their anniversary—that's why they were in Rome with us. He's in love with his wife. It was stupid of me, I know—I'd probably had too much champagne.'

She'd been tense, she remembered, about being there at all, feeling that in attending any Rossetti function she was somehow being disloyal to Neil.

'But he was so embarrassed about me being in his room I only said what I did for a joke, because I heard someone— you—walking by.' And even then that air of command and smouldering sexuality had made an unconscious impression upon her, slashing through her nerve, which was why she had giggled like some inane schoolgirl after he'd gone by.

'So why didn't you tell me before?' He moved closer to her, one hand coming to rest on one of the pillars that graced the elegant room.

'Would you have believed me?' she whispered.

The hard query in his eyes told her that he wouldn't have. She wasn't even sure he believed her now.

'I wouldn't steal from *anyone*,' she stressed, adding on a little pointed note of defiance, 'Least of all you.'

The movement of a black eyebrow acknowledged that spark of spirit, although, in truth, she was close to breaking down, to releasing this aching devastation and disillusionment at the destruction of all her idealistic, adolescent dreams. Julian was a criminal—a thief. And maybe she had already known days ago that she would never marry him. Nevertheless, it still hurt.

'What are you going to do?' If there was a hint of supplication in her voice, she didn't care. She felt drained, weary, beaten by the events of the day. 'I mean...to Julian.'

'Dismiss him.'

'And then?'

He dropped his hand from the pillar, his slow strides bringing him disconcertingly closer to her. 'That depends. I shall have to take advice from my legal office.'

Chelsea's throat worked nervously above the V of her blouse. 'And me?' She couldn't believe that he wouldn't enjoy indicting her in any way he could.

'Yes, Chelsea.' Sensuality overlaid the contemplation in his voice as he came to a standstill in front of her. 'What am I going to do with you?'

He wanted her. He could try and bribe her into surrender by promising leniency in exchange for the ecstasies of his bed—because it would be ecstasy. Shamefully, she didn't even need to like him to acknowledge that. Strangely, though, basic intuition told her that he wasn't a man to stoop to those levels, even when he said quietly, 'Stand up.'

The pulse in her throat beating frantically against her pale skin, she obeyed, and then virtually collapsed against him, as her knee had stiffened up so much.

He caught her instantly, her weight nothing to him as one arm went under her legs, lifting her off the ground.

'Why didn't you tell me you were hurt?' He sounded angry, but it was anger of a different kind now.

'I'm not. I don't want this,' she said abjectly as he shouldered his way out of the door. His arms were so dependably strong, that personal scent of him so addictive, that she found herself fighting feelings that, in view of all he thought about her, her violent emotions towards him, were entirely taboo.

'I don't see that you're in any position to argue, he stated with chastening grimness as he started carrying her upstairs. Yet when he laid her gently down on her bed he said, 'You won't be doing anything for a while, so I recommend the only thing you concentrate on tonight is getting some rest.' And she felt like crying at the oddly compassionate note that she almost wanted to believe she had heard in his voice.

She was reading in the lounge with her leg supported by a luxurious pouffe when Julian found her the following morning.

'So you told him.' Standing there in the room that epitomised the affluence which he had hoped to aspire to, he sounded bitter, his expression no less than malevolent.

'I didn't. I was trying to leave,' Chelsea stated categorically. She knew that he had just come from seeing Paolo, that his prestigious client had just swept the ground—and possibly his whole future—from under him, that Riccardo and another man were waiting to drive him away... Where, she didn't know.

'Trying to...!' Miraculously he hadn't known. From his dumbfounded look it was clear that her attempted departure was news to him. 'Was that what all that noise was about last night—how you hurt your leg?' Obviously Paolo had conveyed that much to him at least. 'You stupid...stupid little fool. Didn't you think about the trouble it would land me in?'

She had, but she had imagined that he'd lie his way around it. Besides, she hadn't reckoned on getting caught.

GET FOUR FREE BOOKS AND A MYSTERY GIFT

Return this card and we'll send you four specially selected Mills & Boon Presents™ novels absolutely FREE! We'll even pay the postage and packing for you!

We're making this offer to introduce you to the benefits of the Reader Service: FREE home delivery of brand-new romances at least a month before they're available in the shops, a FREE gift and a monthly Newsletter packed with information.

Accepting these FREE books places you under no obligation to buy. You may cancel at any time simply by writing to us - even after receiving just your free shipment.

▲ TEAR OFF AND POST THIS CARD TODAY ▲

Yes, please send me four free Mills & Boon Presents™ novels and a mystery gift. I understand that unless you hear from me, I will receive six superb new titles every month for just £2.10* each, postage and packing free. I am under no obligation to purchase any books and I may cancel or suspend my subscription at any time, but the free books and gift will be mine to keep in any case.

(I am over 18 years of age).   P6KI

Ms/Mrs/Miss/Mr _____
                                    BLOCK CAPITALS PLEASE

Address _____

_____

_____ Postcode _____

*Prices subject to change without notice.

Get four books and a mystery gift FREE!

SEE OVER FOR DETAILS

POST THIS CARD TODAY

THE READER SERVICE

FREEPOST

Croydon
Surrey
CR9 3WZ

Offer closes 31st May 1997. We reserve the right to refuse an application. *Prices and terms subject to change without notice. Offer valid in U.K. and Ireland only and is not available to current subscribers of this series. Overseas readers please write for details; Southern Africa write to: IBS Private Bag X3010, Randburg 2125.

MPS MAILING PREFERENCE SERVICE

But she said only, 'That was your problem. I didn't want to be involved in any way in what you were doing.'

Julian made that cynical sound down his nose. 'So you threw me to the wolves.'

'Don't be so dramatic,' she breathed, shuddering at his choice of phrase, which brought back all too vividly the nightmare of the early hours—those dogs. She felt bad enough as it was, without being blamed for something which, after all, he had brought upon himself with his own lack of scruples. 'I didn't have to tell him anything. He already suspected something. That's why he got us up here. He knew before last night.'

'So you had a nice cosy chat about it with him, did you?' Julian's tone was hateful, sneering. 'And you were the one who talked about being two-faced! I didn't realise you'd gone so soft on the man.'

There was nothing else she could say that would convince him that she hadn't played a part in his downfall so she didn't even try. Her face pale, heavy-eyed, she ignored his last remark, taking a little red object from the pocket of her trousers.

'Here,' she said, handing it to him. 'I think you'd better have this.'

It was the box he had given her on the night they had got engaged, with the little ruby and diamond cluster inside.

He flicked it open, looked disdainfully at her ring and snapped it closed again. 'So that's it, then,' he said.

She didn't answer. This whole episode had shocked her into a kind of numbness, so that even ending her engagement didn't have any power to hurt.

'He said that you wouldn't be able to travel when he told me to get the hell out of his house just now, that you'll be stuck here for at least a few more days. That's very convenient, isn't it? I mean—just you and him in this lovely big house.' One sneering glance took in the beautiful room, with its classical pillars and colourful rugs and the tasteful paintings that adorned its predominantly plain walls. 'That's a very convenient little set-up, isn't it? So what does this do?' He was bouncing her ring box on his open palm. 'Allow you to take yourself off with a clear conscience into his bed?'

'Don't be so ridiculous!' Colour crept up her throat into her cheeks, induced by the shame of her unwelcome attraction to the other man.

'Ridiculous? Me?' Julian gave a derisory snort. 'Why don't you admit it? You fancy him like hell—and that's what's so pathetic! You fancy him even though you think he's a swine for all he did to Neil.'

I do not! she wanted to cry out, wanting to convince herself if not Julian, but the words just wouldn't come. Instead, fighting for calm above the remorse and shame and bewilderment that she was feeling, she said steadily, 'I think you'd better leave.'

'Yes, the truth of it stinks, doesn't it?' he said harshly, convinced by her lack of denial. 'Oh, don't worry—I'm going! And I might not be quite the pillar of rectitude you imagined you'd got yourself engaged to but at least I'm not yet quite as bent as you are. You're sick, Chelsea!' And, on that complimentary note, he left.

After he had gone she felt unbelievably depressed. She knew he'd only been taking out his frustration on her, but was anything of what he'd said actually true? Was her fascination for Paolo merely a purely physical response to an indisputably attractive male? Or was Julian right—was there something wrong with her...?

Anxiously she flipped open the English magazine that she had been looking at before he had come in, to try and take her mind off things. An article on dairy farming was written blithely enough to hold her interest for a while until she turned over a page and saw the name 'Rossetti' splashed in gold across a midnight sky. The allure of the model in white chiffon was oozing the sensuality of Dulcibella.

Strange, she thought, how one seventeen-year-old—one she was never likely to meet—was responsible for her being here initially. Yet Dulcibella Rossetti could hardly be blamed for the utter chaos that Chelsea's life was in now, for her failure to see Julian for exactly what he was, and for the umpteenth time since the previous afternoon, when he'd divulged everything to her, she knew only an immense relief that she hadn't married him. Only now, too, could she admit to herself that that relief was what she had felt beneath her hurt pride when he hadn't turned up for the wedding. And yet if Dulcibella hadn't spread those lies and Paolo hadn't already had his suspicions...

She shuddered, not wanting to think about it, and, needing to absorb herself in something else, she went and fetched the sketch-pad that she had bought on her first day there from her bedroom and hobbled back down to the lounge.

The day had turned overcast again, the air heavy and oppressive, and, grateful for the villa's air-conditioning, she sat down at the table in front of one of the long, arched windows and proceeded to sketch the lake.

Some time during the morning someone came to collect the hired car. She heard it pulling down the drive, its engine noise die away, and it was like the final door closing on a definite era of her life, on everything she had trusted, believed in—which, of course, she thought wistfully, was only the case because of the way she was feeling at the moment.

A rumble of thunder seemed to rock the house, and before long the rain was coming down in torrents. With a little shiver, she thought of Paolo. Maria had said that he'd flown off somewhere that morning by private helicopter and Chelsea suspected that his trip would be to do with Julian.

How long did these things take? Would he even be back today? She wasn't familiar with the amazing mobility of the mega-rich, and when she found herself giving more thought than she wanted to to the fact that he might be up there in the sky at that very moment swiftly she closed her mind against it, assuring herself that the Paolo Rossettis of this world were nothing if not invincible.

Indeed, she heard the low growl of his car before too long, and looked up from her drawing after a while, aware of those slow, confident footsteps over the cool mosaic.

'No, I'm afraid the weather didn't detain me,' he said wryly. Perhaps he thought that she'd been hoping it would. His jacket was hooked over his shoulder and there were splashes of rain on the short-sleeved, impeccable white shirt. 'How are you feeling?' He almost sounded as though he cared.

Tucking her hair back behind an ear, Chelsea rubbed her knee with her other hand. 'It hurts like hell—but I'll live.' And because that, if nothing else, wasn't troubling her as much as it had the previous night, she added, 'At least I can walk unaided now. You don't have to soil your hands carrying me any more.'

He came towards her, her brittle tone causing his mouth to quirk, but all he said quietly was, 'I was referring more to your emotional state.'

Her brown eyes clashed with his. She had never considered that he'd known the meaning of the word 'emotion'. Not when he had proved to be such a vindictive adversary—up there in the snow, on the very mountains she was sketching—with Neil.

'I feel fine. I feel like jumping up and down. How do you expect me to feel?' she breathed sarcastically.

'Lousy.' Surprise lined her brow beneath his probing regard of her delicate features. He was studying her pale complexion, the dark circles beneath her eyes. 'It seems...I misjudged you,' he said sombrely.

'Thanks!' She was still unable to cease verbally attacking him. 'I didn't think men like you ever admitted to being wrong, Paolo.'

A spattering of rain hit the windows, like needles thrown carelessly against the glass.

'I'm not above making mistakes, Chelsea.'

Unwittingly her gaze slid down his superb body. 'Really? I thought you were.'

His smile was strangely self-mocking, although he said nothing. He knew how she felt, she realised; would allow her to vent some measure of her wretchedness on him. But at least he couldn't tell how the very sight of him made her pulse race.

With his hair slicked back from the rain and those streaks of grey enhancing the wet bronze of his skin he looked so vital that it took a great effort of will to drag her attention away from him, pretend some interest in what she had been doing before.

'Sketching?' As she started to close her pad, too embarrassed to let him see it, he said, 'No, don't.' And she had to sit there, feeling utterly self-conscious—somehow brutally exposed to him—as he surveyed her feeble attempt to capture the scenery.

'The lake in sombre mood,' he recognised immediately.

Well, that was one thing, anyway. He was only using her sketch, though, she thought, to defuse the situation. Nevertheless, she followed his lead, saying, 'Actually...it's supposed to be at sunset. I'm afraid it isn't very good.'

'I wouldn't say that. You have quite a talent for it,' he complimented her, his interest surprisingly genuine. 'But this isn't quite right.' He was pointing to her experiment with the mountains opposite—the light that she knew she hadn't captured successfully. 'This...' that dark masculine hand indicated the problem '...should be shaded more, with the background paler... May I?'

He was reaching for her pencil and willingly she handed it over.

'Be my guest.' Wasn't that what she had said to him the day he had taken her to that other villa?

Remembering sent a little shiver through her which she knew he'd sensed, even as he said quietly, soberly, 'No, Chelsea. You're mine.'

If only I were! It was that traitorous little voice again, and evoked only by the primitive needs of her sexuality, she assured herself, because she was so drawn by the fierce magnetism of his. In spite of that, though, fascinated, she watched his deft use of her pencil, how the background with which she had struggled and which had remained flat and one-dimensional under her own hand leaped into vibrant realism beneath his.

The talent was in him. He had inherited his father's great artistry, even though he hadn't chosen to follow him into the world of design.

'You see?'

She did, but she was having a job concentrating on his very worthwhile instruction. How could she when he was leaning over her with his hand on the back of her chair, when she could smell the subtle musk of his skin and was wondering what it would be like to lick the raindrops from the silky hairs feathering his arm?

'I see.' How could two words be born so tremulously? She sent a tentative glance up at him, recognising with something like shock the hard desire in those dark eyes looking down into hers.

Caught for a moment under some spell that was too strong to resist, her lips parted in unwitting provocation. Clinging to his scent, her breath trembled through her lungs, every part of her weakening, wanting to turn into him, craving the brutal assault of his kisses, the consequences of a passion that later she would regret, but whose dark mysteries right now seemed to be driving her insane.

She saw the answering response in his eyes, sensed it in the sudden rigidity of his body. Then a sound made them look round—she swiftly, he with only a casual interest.

It was Maria, coming in to gabble something to him in Italian about a message, and the spell was broken, leaving Chelsea shaken and confused by the violence of her attraction to him.

CHAPTER SIX

CHELSEA paused in the letter she was writing to her mother, and then promptly screwed it up. She hadn't contacted either of her parents since the brief telephone call she had made to her mother from Milan to explain why Julian hadn't turned up for the wedding. Then she'd stated only that there had been some dreadful mix-up with Paolo's affairs, but that it was all cleared up and that she and Julian were coming up here to the villa.

She'd felt unable to cope with her mother's overreaction or her father's jibes about marriage if she had told them the whole truth about Dulcibella's false accusations. So how could she even begin to explain now about the terrible thing Julian had done and that their engagement was well and truly off? She couldn't. Not until she had come to terms with it herself.

Tossing the little paper ball into the basket beside the bed, she decided to shake off her troubles with a swim. Yesterday it had been too stormy to go in the pool, even if her knee had been up to it. Also yesterday Paolo had been around, though she hadn't seen a great deal of him after he'd come in as that message from Maria had meant he'd spent most of the afternoon on the phone in his study, sorting out some problem in Milan. Now, this morning, he was out again, though she didn't know where. Consequently, she slackened her steps as she came downstairs, surprised by voices drifting up to her from the hall.

Paolo was back, and he wasn't alone. There was a smartly dressed elderly woman at his side.

Suddenly aware, he glanced up, and Chelsea's pulse throbbed as that assessing dark gaze touched on the pale sheen of her hair and the short white and floral silk robe that exposed the endless length of softly tanned legs; it was a moment of shockingly tangible chemistry, when every nerve reacted to the hard dark power of him, to the restless animal beneath the casual elegance of his clothes.

Then that fierce, molten emotion burning in his eyes— an emotion which she knew had devastated him as much as it had her, leaving her dry-mouthed—had gone, replaced by smooth urbanity as he introduced her to the tall woman beside him.

'Mamma—Signorina Chelsea Adamson. Chelsea—my mother, Sophia.'

'*Signorina.*' The woman moved towards her with the innate grace that she had passed on to her son. Like the grey streaks at the temples, Chelsea noted, which against Sophia's peppered, elegantly styled hair were almost white now. A reflective Mona Lisa smile softened her otherwise strong features. 'So you are...Chelsea Adamson.'

The way she said it made Chelsea dart a glance up at Paolo. What had he been saying about her? Whatever it was, she felt those shrewd feminine brown eyes touch on the hectic colour in her cheeks, then move assessingly to the tall man beside her and back again before their owner commented, 'She's very beautiful.'

Paolo murmured something in Italian which caused the maternal gaze to drop momentarily to the region of Chelsea's left hand, the dark brows to knit, and the swift remark she uttered to Paolo in their own language carried an undertone of...what? Rebuke? Chelsea wasn't sure.

'My fiancé...he had to leave. I shouldn't really be here either. I mean...I had a bit of an accident...' She dropped a glance downwards. 'My knee...' She was floundering, embarrassed at being discussed when she didn't even know what they were saying, what the woman might be thinking.

Paolo, however, was laughing down at her, clearly enjoying her chagrin. 'Why don't you take my mother outside,' he suggested, rescuing her, 'while I go and ask Maria to bring us something to drink?'

It sounded like a good idea and Chelsea readily agreed, if only because it took her out of his disturbing proximity.

'I understand from Paolo that you are her primarily because of Dulcibella.' They were sitting on the terrace on the ornate iron furniture that stood under the shade of a large date palm, surrounded by a vivid spectacle of scarlet geraniums.

Paolo's mother clicked her tongue disapprovingly. 'I am afraid my granddaughter is too much of a rebel, with a total disregard for convention, which is why she chooses to live in Milan with Paolo when her school is finished, instead of in Sicily with me. He is strict—but he also knows how to handle her.' And with a very Latin flourish of hands she added, 'Something I've never been able to do. He was very much a rebel himself when he was younger—and still remains so in some ways—which is probably why he understands her so well.

'Unlike Paolo, however, Dulcibella hasn't yet learned how to direct rebellion into positive and constructive causes, which she will have to do if she is to follow her grandfather and become the valued designer we are hoping she will become. I suppose it is because of all she had to go through—' She broke off, looking, Chelsea thought, puzzled, decidedly uneasy. 'Nevertheless ... she went too far this time. I cannot apologise enough for her behaviour—as I am sure Paolo will have done already.'

Not exactly, Chelsea thought, wondering if this strong and forthright lady knew just how much like Dulcibella—how single-minded and ruthless—her son could be. She hadn't mentioned anything about Julian's breach of trust, though, and Chelsea suspected that she wouldn't, even if she had been told.

Maria came out then, with some delicious-looking fruit punch, and the pouring of the pink liquid suspended the conversation for a few moments with the chink-chink of ice against glass. Somewhere in the garden a bird had started up an unfamiliar trill.

'I must confess to feeling some surprise,' Sophia said, picking a stray pink oleander petal from the folds of her blue voile skirt, 'when he told me that his female guest was the cousin of Signor Adamson.'

Neil? As Maria disappeared Chelsea directed a swift, guarded look at Paolo's mother. So she knew about that little episode. Dubiously, she wondered exactly what the woman had been told.

'It's a small world,' she uttered, feeling awkward talking about it.

'Yes, it is.' Again Chelsea sensed the shrewd calculation behind the dark, intelligent eyes. 'So what do you think of it—our world?'

Abruptly she had changed the subject, waving a graceful hand towards the terraced gardens sloping away to the lake. The bright pinks and reds of miniature begonias stood proudly, their waxy leaves making them seem almost artificial against a bed of loftier blue hydrangeas, while dark crimson roses, their petals soft as velvet, created a fragrant walkway down to the terraces of grapevines. That thick bank of trees at the bottom gave seclusion to the private beach, beyond which the deep sapphire of the lake glittered like a dark jewel.

'It's beautiful.' Imperceptibly Chelsea relaxed, and spent the next few minutes acquainting her with the places that she had visited since she had arrived, deciding that she liked Sophia Rossetti as they exchanged comments about the treasures of some of the villas that were open to the public in the region, the various resorts around the lake, the vast contrast with Milan.

Eventually, Sophia said, 'Every time Paolo invites me here I expect him to announce his intention to marry.' Her expression was almost wry as she went on, 'I imagine you've met Elena.' She gave an elegant little shrug, ice-cubes tinkling against the glass she was holding. 'Until now I was certain that he would marry her.'

Elena? Chelsea stared at the drink that she had just picked up, running a finger over the condensation frosting the outside of the glass. Was she the one earmarked to share the huge Rossetti empire, Paolo's affections? she cogitated, a surge of mixed emotions confusing her as much as Sophia's 'until now'. If he intended to marry Elena, why was he stalling? Or was it an imperfection of phrase on Sophia's part? she wondered as she drank the cold, fruity punch, unable to control a throb of some unwelcome excitement in assuring herself that Sophia's English was perfect.

'Are you hoping he'll marry her?' It was all she could think of to say as she replaced her glass on the ornately cast iron table, pushing aside the strange emotions that made her disinclined to discuss the matter and that put the suggestion of a tremor in her voice.

'Do you think I should?'

She started, surprise causing her to knock over a plastic bottle of sun-lotion on the table as she realised that Paolo had overheard. 'Would it somehow bring you... satisfaction... to see me married?'

He was smiling innocently down at her pinkening cheeks. Satisfaction wasn't what he'd meant at all. Peace of mind, protection—and from her own crazy attraction to him! she thought—that was the message he was conveying, that lapse in his vocabulary deliberate and well chosen and only because Sophia was listening.

'Surely my opinion isn't what counts?' she uttered pointedly, her eyes guarded, her pulse hammering because he'd changed while he'd been inside. Now he was wearing only the dark swimming shorts he'd been wearing that first day, when he'd come back and surprised her here alone. Her silent gratitude that at least this time she wasn't by herself proved premature when Sophia rose, preparing to go in.

Don't go! The woman turned, frowning slightly, and, mortified, Chelsea thought she had uttered that little plea aloud.

'You don't have to, do you?' she asked amiably, in a desperate endeavour to keep Paolo's mother with them.

'I am afraid I must, *signorina*.' If Sophia noticed the panic in her voice, the trembling of her smile, she gave no sign of it. 'At my age, sitting in the sun no longer offers the same joy and sense of freedom as it did. Also, when I was young one could not enjoy the company of the opposite sex without a chaperon—much was the pity.' What was there beneath that ruminative perception—suspicion, wry acceptance? Both? 'Paolo, see she doesn't burn—her skin is very fair. I look forward to seeing you later, Chelsea.'

Alone now with Paolo, Chelsea sent him a surreptitious glance from behind her sunglasses, watching as he tossed down a towel, poured himself some punch from the jug.

'What have you been saying to her about me?' Her tone carried a subtle accusation.

'Saying to her?' That softly accented voice was casual, almost distracted.

'Yes, saying to her. She didn't have to spell it out to make it obvious that she thought that you and I were—'

He laughed when she couldn't say it. 'Were what? Lovers?' he offered in softly mocking tones.

'Don't be ridiculous,' she breathed, glancing away to the craggy peaks of the mountains opposite, her heart thumping like mad.

'Is it ridiculous, Chelsea? Is it any more ridiculous than saying that I've been very unwise in ever inviting you here? That that combination of beauty and—if I may say so—innocence is far too much, too potent not to turn the sanest man's head?'

'Innocence?' She laughed tensely. 'You didn't think me so innocent before.'

His breathing seemed to still. 'Are you going to condemn me eternally for that?' She didn't answer, the leaves of the date palm casting shadows across her face as she lifted her chin in silent belligerence, so that he said softly, 'You're determined to uphold your private vendetta with me, aren't you, Chelsea? I wonder why?'

A flush burned her cheeks at the distinct sensuality in his voice and she turned away, murmuring, 'You can wonder all you like.'

His laugh, like hers, was forced—a superficial expression that concealed some deeper emotion, something smouldering and dark, highly charged. 'I prefer never to leave curiosity unsatisfied.'

She shot him a wary look. 'Paolo, don't.' It was an involuntary little appeal.

'Why not?' He hadn't made a move towards her. He was still standing by the chair that his mother had vacated, as impassive and controlled as if he'd been discussing the times of the ferry. 'I don't have to hide behind lies and a charade of a relationship to conceal what I really feel.' And with a cold assertion he added, 'You were not in love with him.'

An ache of regret—regret for time and energy wasted over someone who hadn't deserved it—mingled with the underlying tension inside of her. 'How do you know what I think, what I feel?' she challenged him, tossing an almost angry glance up at him, her guarded eyes trained on the superb structure of his face with its prominent cheekbones and arrogant nose, on that sensual mouth that was curving now in a coolly indulgent smile.

'Experience,' he said softly.

The bird that had been trilling almost repeatedly took off overhead with a dark glinting of wings.

'And I suppose you've had a lot of that?'

He shrugged, the gesture drawing attention to the jagged scar across his shoulder. 'I'm thirty-four. You can't expect me to have been entirely celibate, can you? No, don't look away, Chelsea.' Because she had, wanting too much to drink in the bronze perfection of his magnificent body, those powerful shoulders and chest, that fascinating arrow of hair that ran below the waistband of his shorts, those solid, hair-covered legs. 'I want you to look at me. As I want to look at you.'

The intensity of need that trembled through his voice whispered of all the passion of his fiery Latin forebears. No Englishman could say it in quite the same way, she thought, that controlled fire in him releasing a trickle of something hot and insidious in her. And with proud awareness of her femininity she lifted her head, glorying in the hot possession of his gaze over the smooth column of her throat, her breasts, the crease of her thighs, which were tantalisingly exposed to him by the high cut of her swimsuit.

Stimulated by his need, she felt the tightening of her breasts before they burgeoned revealingly beneath the snowy Lycra, felt the hard contraction and that moist, tense heat between her thighs.

And he was the last man in the world whom she should feel this way about...

In a swift, spontaneous movement she leaped up from her chair, the sunglasses she discarded missing the table and hitting the flagstones with a dull little clack, though she didn't stop to retrieve them as she ran through the barrier of the oleanders and dived with a headlong splash into the pool.

Oh, heaven! Am I insane?

Her flight was like a red flag to a bull. The turbulence of the water told her that Paolo had plunged in after her, even as she struck out furiously across the pool, punishing herself for the gross disloyalty of her thoughts, of her feelings—if not towards Julian any longer, then most certainly towards her cousin.

'You should know that evasive action like that will only incite me.' He was breathing fast as he swam hard up behind her. 'You can't run away from it, Chelsea.'

No, because he wouldn't let her, she realised, gasping as he caught her by the shoulder, pulling her with him, so that she beat at him with hard yet ineffectual fists as they touched down in the shallower end of the pool.

Even there the water came way above her breasts, so that it was only his hands on her waist that were holding her steady.

'Let me go!'

'No,' he answered with frightening determination. 'Why are you deceiving yourself, Chelsea? Everyone else can see what's happening between us. My mother. Maria. I think even that fiancé of yours suspected something.'

'No!' She was struggling in his grasp, fighting the attraction he spoke of so liberally, the warmth of his nearness, his strength, but, above all, her own heightened susceptibility. 'I'd never have cheated on Julian for you!' she breathed, though her words had a hollow ring to them, even to her own ears.

'Then why did you respond to me, Chelsea? Why—if your engagement meant as much to you as you'd like me to believe it did?'

She couldn't answer that, only silently acknowledging that she could never really have loved Julian in the way a woman should love the man she intended to marry. 'You made it rather difficult for me to put up much resistance!' Pride and panic forced her into blaming him for her own shaming weakness for him, making his mouth pull grimly. Water was dripping from his hair onto the wet bronze of his shoulders.

'It wasn't me you were fighting, *mia cara*—and we both know it. It was what I do to you. What you do to me.' The hand he had dragged down was pressed against his chest, so that she could feel the hard thunder of his heartbeat, feel the warm, sensuous velvet of his skin. 'You want me.'

'No.'

Perhaps it was the uncertainty in that breathless negation that gave her away, because suddenly he was pushing her back against the side of the pool and the next moment she was drowning—drowning beneath the hard, insistent hunger of his kiss.

A prisoner of the water and of his strength, all at once she felt her arms going around his neck in willing acceptance of her fate, while the sun beat down with the fierceness of an angry spectator.

'Oh, *cara* . . .' One arm caught her to him, while the other hand was shaping the wet, tangled gold of her hair. Gently his fingers moved along her throat, over the smooth slope of her shoulders, pushing aside the plunging bodice of her swimsuit to reveal one creamy, tumescent breast.

He groaned his appreciation of her, cupping the full, perfect mound in his palm. Her skin was milky-white against the dark strength of the hand that lifted her, accentuating her feminine fullness, unbelievably sensitive as he drew a roughened thumb across the hardening tip.

He muttered a soft expletive in his own tongue. 'You've never responded to Rendell like this, have you? Have you? If you had then nothing would have kept you out of his bed.'

How did he know? If not through being told then surely from the way her breath came quickly from her lungs, from the pleasure that etched lines of need across her face and brought her lashes feathering against her cheeks.

His lips brushed across her sun-kissed lids. 'You kiss with a passion that no Cupid or Psyche could match, *amore*. It's new to you, isn't it, this sort of passion? And you'd be cheating yourself if you imagined you could live without it. Tell me it's me. Show me I'm telling the truth. Tell me, Chelsea.'

She couldn't speak—didn't want to. She only knew that she had never felt so responsive to any man in her life—or so abandoned—as he lifted her up above the glittering water to draw the perfect wet orb into his mouth.

A sea of pink oleander blossoms shielded them from the house, dispelling the fleeting thought that someone might see them. Even if they did, she didn't think she had the will to care at that moment, whimpering the need engendered by Paolo's hard masculine body—small sounds of joy in the spontaneous heat of her desire.

No other man could ever make her feel like this, talk to her like this. This man had been born to be a lover. Her lover . . .

'*No!*' As reason suddenly surfaced she struggled for her freedom, and was granted it as he reluctantly released her. 'I don't want this! Can't you realise that?'

'No, because the way you kiss, your body, everything about you tells me that you do.'

How could she deny it when she had surrendered to him so completely? When the battle raging between her conscience and her physical desire filled her with fathomless self-disgust?

'Because your ego couldn't stand the deflation of accepting otherwise!' Straightening her swimsuit, she struck out in the water again, not needing to get away from him so much as from what he was telling her. Perhaps things hadn't been right between her and Julian. Perhaps that was why it was so easy to fall into another man's arms. But to behave like this . . . so wantonly—she pulled herself up out of the pool—and with Paolo Rossetti of all people!

'Leave me alone!' She kicked off the hand that was closing around her ankle, rolling round with her legs dangling in the water, glaring down at him. 'Can't you understand? If you were the only man on earth I'd still hate myself every time you touched me. I could never feel anything but revulsion for the man who left my cousin for dead!'

For a moment he seemed to blanch beneath his tan. 'Chelsea—'

'Get away from me!'' she shrieked, drawing her legs up as he made a move to detain her, fearful that if he touched her again she would stay, despite all her protestations to the contrary. And she couldn't. Oh, dear heaven, she couldn't! And now, as he caught the wrist that was supporting her on the tile edge, one leg kicked out and caught him squarely in the ribs, making her wince because she'd forgotten about her knee. The blaze of anger on his face nevertheless propelled her to her feet, accelerating her precipitate flight into the house.

An astonished Maria looked up from her dusting at the fleeing, hobbling creature dripping water all over her freshly polished floor. But Chelsea scarcely noticed her, her only thought to get to her room.

How could she? she thought, self-hatred creeping through her like some deadly plague, though her legs felt weak and her breasts were still swollen and sensitive from the lethal seduction of Paolo's mouth and hands. How could she have let him do those things to her? How could she forget how brutally and unpityingly he had treated Neil?

Peeling off her wet swimsuit, she dumped it into the basin of her *en suite* bathroom, switched on the shower, and, realising she'd left her negligée in the other room, grabbed a towel and tiptoed naked, rubbing her hair, back into the bedroom, only to stop dead in her tracks.

Paolo was thundering in, throwing the door closed after him. He had on a white shirt over cream trousers, though he hadn't spent time fastening it. Nor had he wasted time drying himself, she realised, seeing the dark, damp patches on his clothes, the way the garments clung to him. The mere fact that he had put something on, however, only heightened the embarrassment of her own nudity.

'Don't you ever bother to knock?' As she brought down the towel that was too small to do anything but clutch in front of her her tart query belied the fear in her dark irises— fear that perhaps she had driven him too far in more ways than one out there, because he looked positively menacing, his hard masculinity a threatening intrusion in the ultra-feminine room.

'I thought that self-demeaning little act outside deserved the same lack of respect,' he ground out, coming towards her.

He meant kicking him, and with an arrogant lift of her chin, though her insides felt like jelly, she said, 'What do you want? Retribution?'

'Why not? It's only what you'd expect of me, isn't it?' Deliberately his eyes were making a feast of the softly golden flesh that wasn't concealed by the towel, which was most of her, she realised; and despite his hard, insolent scrutiny she felt that familiar, betraying heat tingle through her body. 'Poor Chelsea. You hate me and yet you're burning up with the desire to have me inside you, aren't you?'

'Stop it!' She pressed her arms hard against her breasts to conceal their traitorously burgeoning betrayal. 'You're obscene!'

'Am I? Because no man has ever spoken to you like this before? Made you face up to the reality of that wild nature?'

'Don't!' Head lowered, she clamped her hands over her ears and shut her eyes, wanting to blot out the sight and sound of him and—heaven help her!—his grossly stimulating words, her heart pounding as she waited for the inevitable—his claim on what he knew he had already conquered.

'Put this on.'

Surprised, Chelsea opened her eyes, catching the flimsy negligée which he had plucked off the bed, and hurriedly she complied, fastening it around her with fingers that shook.

'As much as I like to look at you, I can't concentrate on what I have to say to you while you're wearing nothing, and there's so much that you're going to have to realise.'

'Paolo, please . . .' It was a desperate entreaty against the relentless cascade of the water in the shower. 'Please . . . just go.'

He moved closer, having no intention of doing anything of the sort. 'Why? So you can pretend that didn't happen in the pool this afternoon—at that villa a few days ago?' he ground out, forcing Chelsea's eyes to close, a groan escaping her at the shame of her actions. 'It did. So you'd better face up to it.'

'Why? So you can gloat over your conquest? Isn't that how you get your kicks—out of hurting people?'

'Why ask? You seem to know.' His face set in implacable lines, he brushed past her, went into the shower and snapped off the switch. The silence was ominous, broken only by the sound of the water trickling away. 'You, *mia cara*,' he said, coming back, 'are so naïve.'

'Naïve about what?' she demanded, picking up the discarded towel and rubbing her damp hair for something to do.

'About your beloved cousin, for one thing.'

A little shiver of unease quivered through her. What had Julian said? That Neil was no saint?

She laughed tightly, shrugging off her momentary lapse of faith in the cousin she adored like a brother. 'And I suppose you knew him better than I do,' she quipped sarcastically.

He shrugged. 'Maybe I simply wasn't blinded by love as you are.'

Tight-lipped, Chelsea tossed the towel down onto the pale satin of the bedspread. 'Love? What do you know about love?' she challenged him, in bitter defence of her cousin.

'Enough to know that what you felt for Rendell was not worth the paper it was going to be written on.'

'We're not talking about Julian and me!' she snapped with a toss of her damp, tangled hair.

'Aren't we?'

'No.'

'No.' His lips compressed with that almost mocking negation. 'We're talking about your judgement of men. Rendell was no more right for you than Neil Adamson was for Milan.'

'He would have been—if you'd given him a chance. But no, you had to make that hostile bid against him, didn't you? Take everything he had. And why?' With hands on her hips, she glared angrily up at him. 'Because you couldn't take him stealing a woman away from you.'

His gaze tugged cursorily over her soft contours, emphasised by her belligerent stance. 'Is that what he told you?'

Not in so many words. No one had given her an in-depth account of the relationship that Paolo had devastated along with her cousin's livelihood. 'He didn't have to. It was obvious to everyone by the state he was in when he came home. What was it? Revenge? Or just bruised masculine pride?'

He laughed—a cold, mirthless sound that went right through her. 'If you think that's all there was to it, you're even more naïve, *mia cara*, than I first thought.'

'Not too naïve to know that when you'd finally taken everything from him you took yourself off on a skiing holiday without a glimmer of conscience, and that he nearly lost his life on that mountain because of you. It was your fault that he was even up there that day.' Because he had been determined to find Paolo—confront him face to face with the way he had been so effectively and unscrupulously taken over.

'He came after *me*!' he rasped, jabbing a finger at his chest. His expression was hard, relentless, angry. 'He was a good skier. He knew what he was doing. He was as responsible for his own safety as I was for mine. He'd had access to the weather reports that day. He knew there was avalanche danger. It was his shouting that got him into trouble. When it started to slide there was very little I could do.'

'So you hit him.' The statement hung as a poignant accusation in the air.

'Yes, I hit him.' He wasn't even trying to deny it. 'But only for his own benefit.' There was no contrition, no remorse in his voice.

'What benefit was that, Paolo?' She looked at him obliquely, her eyes darkly accusing. 'So he'd know never to look at a woman of yours ever again?'

A cold smile touched his lips. 'How innocent you are.' The casual brush of his fingers against her cheek had her recoiling in shock and disgust.

'Don't touch me!'

'It's a bit late for that, isn't it?' His embarrassing reminder brought a vermilion hue to her cheeks. 'And, contrary to what you want to believe, I didn't strike your cousin in anger—though heaven only knows I felt like it! He was panicking and in danger of getting us both killed. I know those mountains like I know my own mother. I've been skiing them since I was six years old. We had next to no chance up there. I had no choice but to render him unconscious to prevent us both being smothered.'

'And then you left him,' she uttered, aggrieved, wanting desperately for him to deny it. But he didn't—because he couldn't, she thought achingly as that bare chest lifted and he looked about to say something, then checked himself. 'You hated him that much?' Her incredulity was tinged with pain. 'He was alone, barely conscious—you said so yourself—and if he hadn't managed somehow to crawl under that ledge . . .' A small sob escaped her. 'He said you just wanted to save your own skin.'

That inscrutable gaze flickered across her face. A complexity of emotions darkened those beautiful irises, but he said only, 'Believe it if you want to.'

That was the trouble, though. She didn't want to. 'Neil wouldn't lie,' she said sadly, nevertheless—a remark that pulled Paolo's mouth in a humourless gesture.

'And of course you've already made up your own mind as to the kind of man *I* am,' he informed her caustically. 'Only, I think it appropriate to straighten you out on one minor matter. The woman your cousin was sleeping with wasn't of any particular importance to me, though she was to someone—someone who loved her enough to put his car over a cliff when he discovered she was having an affair. She was nothing to me, *mia cara*. Nothing—beyond my elder brother's wife!'

CHAPTER SEVEN

CHELSEA felt as though she had been punched in the solar plexus.

'His *wife*?' she whispered, shocked. Through the open window the tinkling of a church bell came distantly across the lake.

'That's right. Gina and Neil.' There was no mistaking the bitterness in Paolo's hard, clipped words. 'Together they managed to destroy my brother's life.'

'No.' She was shaking her head. She couldn't believe it. Vaguely now, though, she recalled, a long time ago, hearing something about an accident in the Rossetti family. She'd been too young at the time to take any real interest in people who, after all, had been unknown to her.

'I'm sorry, Chelsea—but you were going to have to know some time. I couldn't believe it when Rendell told me you didn't know.'

A line puckered her brow. She was still shaking her head. If it was true, then she could understand why Julian had said Neil was no saint, why her parents always changed the subject whenever she brought it up. Because he knew. They all knew...

'No one ever told me.' She looked at him, hurting, bewildered. 'Neil...he never said anything...' Her sentence tailed off, her expression growing more pained. How could he have misled her? How could any of them?

'I doubt that he was very proud of it.' Paolo's voice was harsh. 'It was probably better to wallow in the delusion that I was responsible for everything he lost. You see, I was the one who found them together. I came back from a business trip and discovered them carrying on·their sordid little liaison in my own house. When Gina knew her affair had been discovered, she dropped Adamson like—I think

119

you say—a hot potato. I think she was more afraid of what I might do to her than of my actually telling her husband.

'But I didn't tell Giorgio. I didn't have to. As it turned out, he already knew. I'd wondered until then why he was spending so much time away from home, from his job. He was managing the marketing side of things at the time. He couldn't let her go, but neither could he live with her. That's what he'd written in the last letter he ever sent to her. The following day his car was found at the bottom of a cliff halfway along the Amalfi coast.'

'I'm sorry.' It sounded trite, ineffectual.

He shrugged. 'One learns to accept.'

But he hadn't, she thought, torn by conflicting emotions, because it was *her* cousin—the cousin she loved dearly—who had brought such terrible grief to Paolo's family. And the anger and bitterness was still in him, in everything he said and did, and it was, she realised now, only compounded by her being there. 'No wonder you wanted to destroy him,' she murmured with a little shiver.

'Yes.' His shuddering response made her flinch. 'I wanted desperately to destroy him for the pain he'd caused—not just to me but to Dulcibella, and especially my mother.'

'But it couldn't have been all his fault.' She found herself trying for what even she felt was an inexcusable defence. 'Gina must have been willing—'

He gave a snort of mock amusement. 'Oh, yes, I'm pretty sure that she was more than willing. Neil Adamson had a charm that was difficult for women to resist—even one who had been happily married for thirteen years. Yes, I wanted to destroy him, but I didn't. It was his involvement with Gina that contributed largely to his downfall. He lost his head until it affected his judgement, his perception of everything else. In business one can't afford to become complacent, careless. Your cousin did—and had to pay the price.'

'Which you collected.' And with relish, she couldn't help thinking, though the small degree of accusation in her voice drew a grimacing response from Paolo.

'Being swallowed up by my organisation was the lesser of two evils. He made an unwise decision that backfired on him and he owed money—a great deal of money. He couldn't have survived without someone else taking over the company, paying off the creditors. And at least with me he still had his passage home.'

'And Gina?' she asked tentatively, deciding that if she'd been in her shoes she would have wanted to have put as much distance between herself and Paolo as she possibly could.

'Gina went to America,' he answered, confirming it. 'And I took over responsibility for Dulcibella. She had never got on that well with her mother anyway, and Gina was only too pleased to hand over guardianship of her daughter to me. I'm afraid the tragedy of my brother's death has had a rather adverse effect upon Dulcibella.'

'I'm sorry,' Chelsea sympathised, recalling that same cynicism in him when he had spoken about marriage that first day she had met him. And no wonder, she thought, after something like that! And especially when he'd believed her to be guilty of the same crime as her cousin— actively involved in ruining someone else's marriage. 'Is that why you haven't bothered?' she asked tentatively, with an uncontrolled need to know. Because of what happened to your brother?'

Some half-derisive emotion played across his mouth. 'What do you think?' he drawled, in a way that said she hardly needed to ask. 'Oh, there have been one or two serious involvements in my life. Once—before all this happened—I even got as far as getting engaged.'

'What happened?'

He shrugged beneath the gaping shirt. 'I think we both knew all along that it wasn't what either of us were looking for.'

Chelsea frowned. 'Then why did you propose?'

He laughed. 'I didn't—she did. Anyway, why do you need to ask me that?' He smiled wryly now. 'You know yourself how easy it is to drift into a relationship with someone you aren't wholly in love with.'

She couldn't respond in any way to that. What was there to say?

'So you've remained footloose.' She smiled nervously, deciding that the subject of her past relationship with Julian was best forgotten.

'No,' he said bluntly. 'I've remained sane.'

And that was about as cynical as you could get, she thought, reminded of her father, of her own parents' marriage. Perhaps it couldn't work—two people, two personalities, with different needs, different hopes and expectations, sharing the same roof, the same life. Perhaps it never worked.

'Marriage is a massive step.' She heard Paolo's words as if they were an extension of her own thoughts. 'I believe it's important to get it right. It is not a thing to be entered into lightly.'

Chelsea shuddered inside, too conscious of the dreadful mistake that she herself had come so close to making. No, he wouldn't be taken in as she had been; he wouldn't have been so trusting. And not just with Julian, she thought self-deprecatingly. But with Neil as well.

'Poor Chelsea.' Her pain must have conveyed itself to him because his hand lifted to the delicate structure of her jaw and he said softly, 'You've really had a rather raw deal, haven't you?'

The caress of his hand against her cheek was too disturbing, forcing her eyes to close against its dangerous sensuality.

'What about Elena?' she ventured tremulously, wondering why she was even bothering to ask. As soon as she could travel she'd be on the plane home and, for her, Paolo Rossetti would have to cease to exist.

A dark cloud, dark as the night, seemed to hover over the future, and it had nothing to do with her broken engagement to Julian.

'Elena and I...' He inhaled deeply, his hand falling away from her. 'We have an understanding.'

Chelsea frowned. An understanding? That implied that they were lovers, didn't it?

Her own hungry emotion seemed to be mirrored in the eyes that locked on hers—a silent, mutual communication of something reckless and definitely taboo.

'I think you'd better go,' she whispered.

He seemed about to say something, swaying almost imperceptibly towards her. But he obviously thought better of it and, with a subtle nod, strode out, closing the door.

What an absolute mess! she thought. All along she'd believed that Neil had been the injured party, and she had despised Paolo with an intensity that was shameful now to comprehend, and all the time...

Despair threatening to crush her, she moved over to stare unseeingly out across the garden. First Julian, now this...

The agony of truth lay like a lead weight in her chest. Why hadn't anyone told her, when it was obvious to her now that everyone had known? Her mother. Her father. Julian. Probably even Murray. Why had they all thought fit to keep her in the dark? she reflected torturedly. To protect her from the truth? She had been only seventeen at the time, it was true. But why hadn't anyone said anything to her since?

Propelled by a need to put the matter straight, to redeem, if only in her own mind, the man of whom she had thought so badly, she now had the strength to write to both her parents and, abandoning her shower, she sat down to state the cold, plain facts about Julian, to tell them that the wedding was off and that she also knew the truth about Neil.

She kept the letters as emotionless as she could, careful not to blame either of them for shielding her from the facts, but as she finished the letters and folded them into their respective envelopes for Maria to post she couldn't help feeling doubly hurt that they had both lied to her, if only by omission—couldn't help feeling doubly betrayed.

* * *

The following day brought a cloudless blue sky and brilliant
sunshine, and when Paolo invited her out on the boat,
Chelsea, aware that Sophia was going too, readily agreed.

She hadn't been near the beach since the other day when,
out there on the raft, she had first learned what Julian had
been up to, and she shuddered as the boat purred past it.
Then, looking up and seeing the speculative look that Paolo
shot her from the wheel, she wondered if he could read her
mind.

Between her cousin and her fiancé, there was little left
for any member of the Rossetti family to like about her,
she thought, wearing both men's guilt as if it were her own.
Yet Sophia was pleasantness itself, showing only the utmost
cordiality towards her, joking about her son having his sea-
legs before he could walk as Paolo drew up alongside one
of the waterfront hotels of their own resort where she
stepped ashore, wishing Chelsea 'a very nice day'.

'Aren't we going ashore too?' From the rail Chelsea
looked quizzically towards Paolo, who was preparing to turn
the boat lakewards again. 'I mean . . . I thought we were all
staying together.'

'Did you?' He laughed at her obvious unease.

'You could have told me before,' she said tightly.

'And you would have done what? Decided not to come?'

She couldn't be so ungracious as to say that she probably
wouldn't have. Besides, that would have been like telling
him how disquieting she found his company. 'If I hadn't
come,' she said levelly, feasting her gaze on the heart-
stopping strength of his profile, 'then you could have taken
Elena.'

'Elena's in Milan.' The boat's engines roared into full
throttle now.

So she would have to do? Maybe that was what he wanted
her to think, she cogitated as she felt the cool spray on her
face, the wind in her hair.

'Is it me you don't trust? Or yourself?' he queried,
amusement crinkling the eyes he turned in her direction.

If only he knew! she thought, her chin lifting in silent rebellion as she glanced away.

'Stop fighting me,' he advised softly as they cruised out into the widening expanse of the lake. The pale buildings on the other side were almost obscured today, shrouded in a heat haze. 'For all you're determined to believe it, I'm not your enemy. And I had no ulterior motive for bringing you out here today. I knew my mother wanted to meet her friend for coffee in that hotel, and if you had wanted to go with her I'm sure she would have been delighted, but as you've been virtually immobilised for the past couple of days I thought you might appreciate something a little more active.'

'Oh,' was all she could say to that, surprised to realise that he had had her interests at heart. She couldn't help feeling awkward with him, though—with both of them— even without the obvious disturbances he caused in her whenever they were alone. And with a glance back towards the café-bar, under the porticoes of the hotel where they had dropped Sophia she said on a self-denigrating note, 'I'm surprised she speaks to me at all, considering who I am. I know she was surprised to find me here—she said so. How badly did she take it about Neil and—what was her name?—Gina?'

The muscles in those tanned arms bunched as his hands tightened around the wheel.

'How would you have expected her to have taken it?' he rasped through clenched teeth. 'Giorgio was the apple of her . . . heart.'

'Eye.'

'What?' The furrow between his eyebrows reflected the tension in him as he glanced across at her, standing near the shining chrome of the rail. The wind was whipping her hair across her face now.

'It's eye.' She raked the hair back with one hand. 'The apple of her eye,' she said, her voice rising above the wind in her correction of his almost flawless English. 'And

Julian? I suppose she knows all about what happened with
him as well.'

He was silent as he steered the powerful vessel into a
wide arc, engines growling, its sparkling wake curving away
behind them in a bow of agitated white foam.

'I haven't told her your fiancé was embezzling,' he said
above the engine noise a few moments later, 'if that's what
you mean.'

'Why not?' she shot back, looking defensive, sounding
aggrieved.

The brevity of his glance down over her red T-shirt and
white shorts was still enough to send her senses into an-
archy. He eased back on the throttle. The engine noise
whittled to a soft purr. 'I thought you were feeling bad
enough as it was.' There it was again, that surprising el-
ement of concern for her. 'I simply told her that when you
arrived you had a fiancé—and now you don't.'

Chelsea gave a nervous little giggle. 'Is that why she
looked at you as though you were totally responsible for it
the day she arrived?'

That hard, masculine mouth moved in a wry grimace. 'I
would not deliberately set out to ruin anyone's engagement, Chelsea.' And more rigidly he added, 'Or their
marriage.'

As Neil had? He didn't have to say it. His smouldering
hatred for her cousin would always be with him—like that
cynicism he couldn't help expressing towards marriage itself.

'You know now why I showed so little appreciation for
the fact that you were wearing his ring.'

Because he had thought her loose, as well as money-
grabbing and dishonest, and her response to his own ad-
vances had only reaffirmed his opinion, she thought
cringing, understanding all too clearly now his past contempt for her.

'My mother, however, is a director of several of our
companies. If Julian's fraud is proved through legal
channels . . .' He had cut the boat's engine and he made a

typically Latin gesture with his hands, leaning there on the wheel. 'It will probably be inevitable that she will find out.'

Of course, Chelsea thought, accepting that people—friends, relatives—might eventually come to hear the truth about her broken engagement to Julian. She couldn't help feeling sorry for Julian's family, though, especially his mother. For all her pretensions and snobbishness, Muriel Rendell didn't deserve a humiliation—a heartbreak—like that.

'What about me?' Chelsea's voice had dropped almost to a whisper. 'What was it that made you believe me so easily?'

They were barely moving now, barely drifting on the sun-streaked water. They weren't that far from the shore on the starboard side, and an interesting white villa with pointy spires. An elegant attendance of stone statues graced its well-manicured lawns, and trimmed cypress trees, shaped into stalagmites, pointed dark green fingers to the sky.

Paolo laughed softly. 'Who said I did?'

Chelsea's eyes widened. Was he teasing? 'You mean you're still checking me out?' She laughed uncertainly.

'*Chucking* you out, over the side, if you don't relax and start to enjoy the trip, which I can see is totally wasted on you.' There was a spark of playfulness in his eyes.

'Didn't Julian tell you I had nothing to do with it?' She doubted if her ex would have admitted it to her even if he had.

'Yes.' Paolo's tone and expression had sobered.

'But you believed me before then.' She studied him obliquely, trying to make him out. 'You did, didn't you?'

He shrugged. 'Perhaps,' he said, 'it was the way you looked, acted the previous night after I'd dragged you up off that grass. So shocked, so...bewildered.' And quietly he added, 'Perhaps I wanted to.'

The water lapped against the boat, the sound as sensual as the note in Paolo's voice had been.

'Why?' she whispered, knowing the question could lead her into an area in which she wasn't sure she wanted to find herself, yet compelled to ask.

'Do you really need to question why?'

Chelsea's throat contracted as he moved away from the wheel.

'You know what you do to me, don't you?' he said.

She took a deep breath, her body pulsing, her eyes wary as the boat dipped as he came over to her.

'Chelsea?'

His voice willed her to look at him, but she didn't dare to as she felt those strong hands on the curve of her shoulders. Her lashes lay against the hollows of her eyes and her breath trembled at the gentle touch of his lips against her forehead, the bridge of her nose, and she felt them move with infinite tenderness across each of her closed lids in turn.

The shoulders that she was clutching were solid, firmly muscled under the soft, casual shirt, and the faint, erotic scent of him beneath the subtlety of his cologne was threatening to drive her wild.

Oh, God! Why did she have to feel like this—and about him, of all people? Granted, he'd had reason for treating her the way he had—and even more reason to hate Neil. And yet always, at the back of her mind, was that one niggling doubt that wouldn't go away...

'No, don't...' She averted her face to avoid the arousing tenderness of his mouth, but he didn't let her go, and tingles ran down her spine as his lips caressed her hairline, whispered into the tangled, silken gold.

'Why, Chelsea? When our mutual chemistries tell us that we were meant to be, that pleasure will only be a word until you and I become lovers. You can't pretend it isn't true, can you?'

'No.' With her forehead touching the dark underside of his chin, the breathless admission seemed not to belong to her but to be spoken by somebody else.

Over his shoulder, she noted absently, in the grounds of that villa, there was a ladder against one of those stalagmitic trees. Gardeners were keeping them in shape, like gigantic church spires straining towards a heaven that could never be reached.

Somehow now she managed to pull free, turning to grasp the rail, taking in lungfuls of air. 'There's too much between us, Paolo.'

'Such as?' He sounded inexorably grim. And when she didn't answer he asked, 'Is it to do with your... cousin?' There was nothing but disdain in the way he spoke about Neil.

Chelsea swallowed, staring out across the open lake and the mountains facing the port side. And when she still didn't respond he suddenly shocked her by asking, 'Were you in love with him? Is that the reason he means so much to you?'

'No! Of course not,' she appended less vehemently, although she remembered her mother saying once that no man would ever be able to live up to her rose-tinted image of Neil. Perhaps that was why no one had wanted to destroy her illusions about him, why no one had told her what had really happened. 'Neil lived with us for a time, so that his mother could work after his father died. Mum and Dad's marriage was always on the rocks. One or other of them was always walking out. But Neil was always there. Always reliable. Always constant.'

'And therefore you looked to him as the only stability in your life.'

Had she? 'I suppose I must have,' she murmured, more to herself than to Paolo, surprised by his immediate grasp of the situation.

'And no one could hear to tell you that he wasn't quite the perfect individual you thought he was.'

She sent a sidelong glance at him, detecting the detestation, barely concealed, in the softly accented voice.

'It hurts,' she said.

'It would.' It was a cool, impassive acknowledgement. He was standing there, his thumbs stuck into the waistband of his trousers. 'Is that why you were so keen to tie yourself down to a man you didn't really love? Because of the insecurities of your childhood?'

'Of course not,' she stressed again, but less hotly now, wondering for the first time if she had—if, in fact, he wasn't right about that as well. 'Anyway,' she uttered rather lamely then, 'anyone can make a mistake.'

'And not admit it, even when they're already aware they're more attracted—physically at any rate—to someone else?'

'That isn't love,' was all she could say to that, her cheeks flaming from the way she always responded to him, even against her better judgement, whenever he touched her.

'I didn't say it was.'

No, he wouldn't. Making love, to him, was probably just an essential and unemotional aspect of his life, she thought, wondering why she should let the thought depress her so much as he swung away from her and put the powerful boat back into motion.

Over the next few days Paolo went out of his way to entertain her, taking her sightseeing, showing her the best vantage points to take photographs, and, at the villa, encouraging her with and advising her on her sketching.

Her knee had healed considerably, and she knew that she should have been making plans to go home. But her reluctance to face her family and friends after all she had been through, coupled with an even greater reluctance to leave the villa, which, she pretended to herself, had nothing to do with Paolo, had her accepting his almost casual invitation to stay on. She had taken three weeks off work anyway—originally to help Julian decorate his flat, into which she'd been intending to move after the wedding—so she had plenty of time to while away.

Of course, Sophia's friendly persuasion had a lot to do with it. Chelsea fooled herself into believing that, since

Paolo's mother seemed to enjoy having another woman around, but deep inside she knew it was that reckless attraction to Paolo that had ensnared her, like an insect lured by the hard incandescence of a lantern that in the end would bring it nothing but regret.

The comparison brought a wry curve to her lips as she came out of the villa to accompany him to a private sculpture exhibition one afternoon.

'You look very...enigmatic,' he commented, just the richness of his tone with that subtle, sexy accent doing funny things to her as he handed her into the car.

'Do I?' She laughed. 'Then I'm sorry to disappoint you. I'm afraid with me, Paolo, you get exactly what you see.'

Too late she realised how her words could be misconstrued, and obviously had been, when he came back mockingly with, 'But I haven't had you yet,' and closed her door as a bright flush suffused her cheeks.

The truth was, though, that he hadn't attempted to touch her, except in the most casual of contacts, since she'd frozen him off on that boat, but his seeming indifference to her, rather than pouring water on her explosive reactions to his sexuality, had only served to detonate them, so that the simplest word, a touch, that lazy twist of his smile set off charges in her that made it almost impossible for her to look at him directly now without the fear of giving herself away.

She was glad, therefore, when the journey to the hotel where the exhibition was being held was only a short one, if only to be released from the confining intimacy of his car.

'Signor Rossetti.'

Everywhere they went, people knew him, Chelsea realised as some young under-manager in the foyer tilted his head in deference to him before sparing an admiring glance for the woman at his side.

She supposed that they did present a striking couple, she being as fair as Paolo was dark. A stealthy glance up at him appreciated how those light, casual clothes emphasised his dark features and the superb lines of his physique as they stopped beside the board next to the lifts, which indicated the location of the sculptures.

'This way.' Just the touch of his hands on her shoulders was enough to send her senses into chaos.

'It's on the fourth floor!' she protested breathlessly as he steered her in the direction of the stairs.

'So?' He laughed. 'Do you have any particular objection to taking some exercise?'

She shrugged—smiled. 'No.' This was how he kept so superbly fit, she decided, aware of how hard he made himself work in the pool each morning, often before anyone else was up. In fact, it was she who showed signs of flagging as they reached the appropriate floor.

'Brute,' she complained amiably when he laughed at her exaggerated pretence of fatigue as he held open the glass fire door for her. 'I'll get my own back sooner or later.'

'That should be interesting,' she heard him comment from close behind her.

She ignored him, though, because his sudden proximity and that faintly personal scent of his, caught as she'd walked under his arm through the door, had impinged too sharply on her senses, and anyway they had reached the room where the sculptures were being shown and where a chicly dressed young woman was handing out leaflets about the exhibits.

It was an interesting hour or so among a fascinating if not entirely pleasing array of bronzes, the theme of which, Chelsea decided, was definitely downbeat.

'What do you think?' Paolo's lowered tone respected the concentration of other viewers as he joined her in studying an intriguing piece on the other side of the room.

The startling impact of his hard vitality after the sordid representation of a tramp she had been surveying almost took her breath away.

'It's...interesting,' she offered, holding her head first this way and that to try and understand what the sculptor was getting at.

'But?'

She met those devastating features again with a wry smile. 'He's no Canova,' she admitted shyly, thinking of the perfect beauty of *Cupid and Psyche* in that villa at Tremezzo.

'Canova was an idealist. This is nearer realism,' Paolo told her with an indicatory toss of his chin. And indeed he was right, because its creator had definitely caught the despair of the beggar and the drug-addict, the pain of a man tearing his hair out to produce a mass of troubled images—his unwanted thoughts clutched firmly in his hand.

'Does it strike too close to home?' he whispered with an ironic smile when he noticed the point at which her absent gaze had stopped.

'Very funny.' Quickly she diverted her attention to one of the less disconcerting pieces. 'Anyway, it goes beyond realism,' she said, unaware of how uncomfortable she looked, because the subjects were designed to shock—ugly caricatures, almost, of the saddest creatures of society. 'It's clever. It's brilliant...' She hesitated, aware that the sculptor was a friend of Paolo's, afraid of saying too much.

'And?' he pressed, inviting her opinion.

'I find it depressing,' she confessed rather tentatively. 'I can't say I like his choice of theme.'

Her reluctance in admitting it seemed to amuse him. He knew she usually spoke her mind. But with an arm across her shoulders he bent towards her, saying, 'I don't think we're supposed to like as much as sympathise.' And in a more conspiratorial whisper he added, 'But no, neither do I.'

His touch seemed to still her pulse before his arm fell casually away from her.

'Do you think we should tell him?' she giggled, struggling to bring her racing adrenalin back under control.

'Oh, he already knows.'

She met his amusement with laughing surprise as they completed their tour of the exhibits. 'And you mean you're still friends?'

He shrugged, smiling down into her astonished features. 'Why not?' he said drily. 'He gives me enough criticism of the products and creations that come out of the Rossetti stable. All adverse mostly,' he joked as they were heading for the door.

'I don't believe it!' Chelsea laughed, returning the *ciao* of the pretty Italian girl who was still handing out leaflets, and whose smile for Paolo, she noticed, could easily have melted stone.

'I think in this case, *signorina*,' a masculine voice suddenly said from behind them, 'it would be more than best not to believe anything the man tells you.'

They turned to meet the laughing, black-bearded face of the man whom Chelsea recognised from the leaflet that she was still holding as Stefano, the sculptor himself.

'He shows nothing but . . . what do you say? . . . contempt for my work.' He threw up his hands in an effusive gesture of mock frustration. 'Seriously . . .' one hand came to rest affectionately on Paolo's shoulder ' . . . this man knows a great deal about art and design, and I value his opinion as I value my life.'

Chelsea laughed, warming to this obviously eccentric acquaintance of Paolo's, but he meant every word, she could tell.

'And you, *signorina*? What do you think of my work?'

Chelsea swallowed, instinctively looking to Paolo for help. What was she supposed to say to that?

'Chelsea . . . she is . . . a romantic,' Paolo intervened while she was still struggling to find a way to be truthful without offending this nice, middle-aged Italian. His effortless diplomacy caused the sculptor to grin.

'My friend . . . he is not always so tactful,' Stefano said sagely, but Chelsea wasn't looking at him.

Thank you, her eyes, held by the dark fire of Paolo's, were saying, that touch of warmth on his lips, that exchange of glances enveloping them in a small, private world—a world of shared secrets, of a subtle yet deepening rapport.

She forced her attention back to something that the sculptor was saying while she tried to reject the pleasure stealing through her from that silent communication with her escort.

She didn't want to be so stirred by him like this. To fall for him like some crazy schoolkid could cause complications all round. That was if he were to return her feelings, which she had no illusions about him doing anyway. Therefore she threw herself into the conversation with the sculptor with an eagerness that surprised even herself.

'My theme shocks you, *signorina*, I can tell,' Stefano said shrewdly after a while. 'But inspiration, you understand, has to come through the soul. Creativity is vision, and vision is something here.' A clenched fist tapped his heart. 'It is insight, understanding—and I understand only too well the plight of these poor creatures. I, too, shared their world—would be sharing it now if it were not for this man here...'

Startled by what he was saying, Chelsea followed his gaze, which had settled with unerring gratitude on Paolo.

'He pulled me up when I was down. Supplied a roof over my head. And he does this not just for me. Though he would not let it be publicly known, this country's unfortunates owe a great deal to Paolo Rossetti's generosity. The old. The sick. The poor—'

'And those who talk too much,' Paolo cut in, clearly unimpressed by the other man's extravagant ramblings about his charitable deeds. And the sculptor laughed, patting him on the shoulder before darting off to speak to someone else. Paolo said drily, 'Stefano likes nothing better than to share his enthusiasm for his ideas with others. Nothing, that is, except using his charm on beautiful women. You must have made his day.'

'He was interesting,' Chelsea admitted as they came into the lobby where the lifts were. She could feel her defences crumbling, shaken to the roots by what she had learned about Paolo. 'And he was right,' she said, warmed by a glowing heat along her veins that sprang from more than just his compliment about her being beautiful. 'You do know a lot about the subject.'

His lips compressed in a wry, almost dismissive gesture. 'It used to be a hobby of mine,' he said unpretentiously, 'before I was forced into accepting full responsibility for the business.'

'Oh, poor you!' She laughed, still trying to take in all that Stefano had told her, her eyes twinkling with anything but sympathy because he had to be worth millions—billions even, until she realised.

Of course. Until his brother's accident there had been two of them to share the load.

Hiding her embarrassment in a continuing show of playfulness, she caught his arm as a lift opened right in front of them and tugged him inside.

'Got you!' she laughed triumphantly as the doors started to close. 'I might gain a stone or two *en route*, but four flights are enough for me for one day!'

Strangely, he responded with only a tight movement of his lips. Perhaps she'd been too forward in grabbing him like that, she thought, keenly conscious of how alone they were now.

Vivid images trespassed on her mind because of something he'd said—images of those dark hands shaping and caressing with tender, infinite skill. But it was the things that the sculptor had told her that were paramount in her thoughts and tentatively, rather breathlessly she blurted out, 'Is it true?'.

'Is what true?'

Why did he look so hard? Sound so distant? 'The things Stefano was saying?'

'If you mean about him sharing a world of beggars and thieves—yes, it's true. He turned to drink after an unhappy love affair. Lost his home and everything he had. But he's doing all right now.'

'Thanks to you.'

'No—thanks to his own effort and determination,' he said, his tone clipped.

'And you,' Chelsea reiterated.

'Yes, well...' He didn't want to talk about it, or anything to do with this other side of his character that she had only just discovered, while she... She wanted to know everything about him, all that there was to know, to start by telling him how wrong she had been that evening when they had been discussing designer clothes and she had called him a hypocrite, but she didn't dare.

As the lift bore them down his features seemed to harshen into a carved mask. He seemed cold and totally unapproachable now. Had it offended him so much that she had stumbled upon this caring side of him? she wondered, and, stealing a glance at him, was startled to notice the sudden pallor under the hard bronze of his tan. There was a dewiness to his skin across the high, intellectual brow, although it wasn't hot in the building. In fact, it was rather on the cool side. Perhaps he was sickening for something, she thought, puzzled.

His eyes were fixed piercingly on the central light in the lift. She could almost feel the tension that seemed to be holding him rigid, and tried to grasp some elusive memory. When had she seen him like that before?

But the lift had stopped, was opening. They were crossing the carpeted foyer where the concierge nodded at them from his desk. And as Paolo, looking more relaxed now, said, 'So you would not be keen to see *Psyche and Cupid* in Stefano's style?' Chelsea remembered.

It had been the day he had been taking her to Como, the day he'd blamed her—uncharacteristically, she'd felt—because he hadn't been able to get out of his car.

CHAPTER EIGHT

IT WAS dark when they returned to the villa, as Paolo had insisted on taking her to dinner straight from the exhibition. Sophia had already retired. The partially embroidered tablecloth on which she had been working in the lounge was neatly discarded, Chelsea noticed, fingering the beautiful needlecraft. Then, hearing Paolo coming back, she strolled out onto the terrace to where he had just been instructing Maria to bring them coffee.

'You get on well with my mother, don't you?' he remarked, joining her, having noticed her appreciating Sophia's exquisite handiwork.

'Yes, I do,' she agreed warmly, although she couldn't look at him as they wandered under the trees. She didn't want to be reminded of how powerfully lean he was beneath the dark jacket that he had donned over the casual shirt and trousers to take her to dinner, because ever since this afternoon, when she had discovered that humanitarian side to him, her physical and emotional responses to him had gone into overdrive. 'She's a very generous-hearted lady,' she added, walking away from him towards the pool.

The lights had come on, shining through the depth of blue water. The wind had changed too, blowing southwards as it always did at night, carrying with it the sweet, powdery fragrance of the oleander.

'I think I should be the one saying that to you, Chelsea.' Sometimes when he spoke her name it was like that first time—sensual, so disturbingly intimate. 'I don't think I thanked you properly for what you did for her yesterday.'

She gave a dismissive shrug, the pool lamps highlighting the pale gold brushing her shoulders.

'It wasn't anything, really.' Sophia had had a blinding headache from sitting too long in the sun, and Chelsea had insisted on helping her to bed. It hadn't been too much to do, phoning Sophia's friends to cancel the arrangements she'd made for that evening and, knowing she'd refused dinner, simply preparing a light meal after the kitchen staff had gone off duty, to entice her to eat.

'If that was nothing,' he said with a strange inflexion in his voice, 'I would like to be around when you were really employing those caring qualities. No, don't run away!' Because she would have, if he hadn't sidestepped to stop her doing so. 'Why are you so determined to avoid any situation in which you find yourself entirely alone with me? Is it, my beautiful Chelsea, because we both know that all I would have to do would be to step forward now...' A stone crunched beneath his foot as he did just that, his smile mocking the panic that was suddenly leaping in her eyes. 'That all it would take would be one touch...'

Her breath caught in her lungs as he slipped an arm around her midriff. Her creamy blouse, tied above the waist, left a few inches of flesh bare above the pale band of her trousers, and the rough fabric of his sleeve and those cool fingers were dangerously arousing on her heated skin. 'You're fighting me now and yet every pore is begging you to surrender. That's why you can't look at me, why you have to close your eyes to hide the way my touch makes you feel—'

Someone running across the terrace made them both turn sharply. Maria suddenly appeared under the trees.

Thank heaven for Maria! Chelsea thought, struggling for composure, realising that she'd been seconds away from proving Paolo right. Now, though, it was obvious that the little maid was distressed—in fact, almost hysterical.

'What is it, Maria?' Paolo asked urgently in his own language as she came up to them. 'For heaven's sake! Get a grip on yourself! What is it?' He had caught her by the shoulders and was having almost to shake her to get some coherent sense out of her. 'Tell me? What's the matter?'

'Oh, *signore! Signore!*' She looked past him at Chelsea, then back to Paolo again, sobbing, tears streaming down

her face. 'I'm sorry, Signor Rossetti. I'm so, *so* sorry...'
Whatever she was sorry about, at last she appeared to be
making sense enough for him to hurry with her back into
the house while Chelsea followed close behind them.

'Oh, *mamma mia*!' She reached the breakfast room at
the same time as Sophia, who had obviously been disturbed by the maid's hysterics and now stood rooted in the
doorway, a shaky hand at her throat. Paolo was looking
stunned, one hand resting on the long wall-to-wall dresser,
the sobbing Maria beside him, staring down at what appeared to have been a delicate, gold-rimmed vessel, now
lying in myriad pieces on the hard floor.

'Oh, *signore*! *Signora*! I will leave! I will go away!' She
was looking, horrified, at Paolo, as though she was half
expecting him to beat her.

'Was it expensive?' Chelsea whispered to Sophia, only
to receive a pale-faced nod in reply.

'Of tremendous value,' the woman found her voice
eventually to utter. 'It was a wedding gift to Gina and
Giorgio, Paolo's brother,' she appended uncertainly, as if
Chelsea didn't know.

'For heaven's sake, Maria, calm down.' Still speaking in
Italian, Paolo sounded surprisingly reassuring, and when
the maid still didn't respond he caught her firmly by her
upper arms, saying even more slowly and concisely, 'It's
only a vase. The main thing is that you weren't hurt...' At
last this seemed to do the trick, his unflappable handling
of the situation finally calming her down enough to bring
her hysteria under control. 'I'll clean this up,' he said gently.
'You go on up to bed.' And with a glance over his shoulder
at his mother he recommended with firm insistence, 'Take
her up. She isn't in a fit state to do anything else tonight.'

Maria's broken sobs could still be heard as Sophia guided
her gently up the stairs.

'You were very understanding,' Chelsea commented,
when he came back from fetching something to sweep the
broken pieces into. She hadn't understood all of what was
being said—she hadn't needed to for her heart to swell with

something way beyond respect for him. 'Sophia . . . told me its history.'

'Yes, well . . .' A brush and dustpan in his hands, he dropped to his haunches to deal with the disaster. 'What's done is done,' he accepted, handling the larger pieces first, but there was an intonation in his voice that told her he regretted what had happened far more deeply than he was letting show.

'Let me help you.'

As she went to pick up one particularly jagged piece, his hand closed swiftly over her wrist.

'No,' he said, prohibiting her. 'The last time there was flying glass around you wound up getting hurt.'

'That was different,' she argued, unsettled by that dark, lean hand that had her pulling hers away. 'I didn't see it coming.'

He was adamant, though, so all she could do was hold the dustpan for him as he began sweeping up the fragments, although as he bent to his task, she had to clench her other hand to stop from reaching out and touching the rich sable of his hair, which her fingers were itching to do.

'There . . .' She couldn't look at him as he brushed the remaining particles into the dustpan, leaving no trace of the disaster. If only the past could be swept aside as cleanly! she thought, and started as he said, 'What are you thinking?'

Meeting the probing directness of his eyes, she swallowed. 'Just that Maria looked as though you were going to flay her alive.' She laughed, her voice strung with tension. 'She seemed terrified of you.'

'Did she?' He relieved her of the dustpan and in one lithe movement emptied its contents into a bin near the fireplace with a sad clatter of glass before tossing it with the brush onto the marble hearth. 'And you, Chelsea . . .' He moved towards her, his steely demeanour a hard contrast with the fine, classical beauty of the nude Greek figure in the alcove behind him. 'Are you terrified of me?'

'Of course not,' she lied, because even on her feet, in three-inch heels, she still felt overwhelmed by his masculinity.

'No?' He laughed, coming closer, his dark, exciting sexuality weakening her, holding her under the spell of its riveting magnetism, until Sophia spoke from the doorway.

'Paolo. Maria—she will be all right. I think I will go back up now.'

'I think I'll join you.'

That far too swift response of Chelsea's hadn't escaped either of them, she realised, seeing the subtle tilt of feminine brows, the mockery on Paolo's lips before she uttered a barely audible goodnight and made to follow his mother.

'Chelsea.' She stopped, her heart doubling its rhythm as she turned round. Why did he have to be so...dynamic? she thought achingly as he took a few paces towards her, her eyes adoring the way he moved, that lean grace, his elegance, everything about him; fear and excitement rising from the knowledge that if he ordered her to stay, she would, if he touched her again, would welcome her own submission. But with his mouth turning at the corners all he said quietly was, '*Buonanotte*. Sleep well.'

She didn't linger to risk uttering a single syllable, not trusting herself to speak.

In her room she stumbled through the darkness, only switching on the small lamp above the mirror in the bathroom. The cold pool of light made her features look pale, her dark eyes wide and hungry, like those of some heroine of history about to face the scaffold for crimes of treason.

Treason. Disloyalty. Betrayal. Driven by impulses beyond her will, she reached for the dark, elongated bottle she'd complained about on her first day there and which still stood on the vanity shelf, and very carefully she pulled out the glass stopper.

The scent of Dulcibella impinged on her with its luxurious sensuality. She had never been tempted to try it—hadn't even smelt it since the night of that launch. On principle!

she thought self-derisively, inhaling the fragrance as if it were some necessary drug, unable to get enough of it. Of *him*. That was what this was all about.

Dear heaven, I love him! The unbidden admission had her clutching the edge of the china bowl in shock, had her gasping as if for air. She wanted to be with him, near him, engulfed by him—had wanted it, if she was honest with herself, since that night when she had first stumbled into his arms.

Smearing perfume along the back of her left wrist, she watched with dangerous fascination as it was absorbed into the throbbing blue vein, pressing her cheek against her scented flesh as though it were his. This betrayal of sorts had started flowing through her veins that night as surely as that glass had grazed her ankle, she thought with a small, ironical grimace, intoxicated by the scent named after a girl who was partly responsible for ruining her wedding—a perfume that women everywhere hoped would make them irresistible to men, while all it did for her was drive her wild for its creator!

She didn't know how she had allowed herself to become so hopelessly and emotionally involved with him, but she had.

Tired, but feeling like anything but sleep, she sat for a long time in the smooth, upholstered chair by the window, listening to the chirping of the crickets, watching as one by one the lights started going out along the lakeside and then, closer to hand, the garden adopting its sleepy mantle when Paolo switched off the outside lights for the night. A few minutes later a door closed on the same floor as hers.

She loved him! That was all she knew. Because how could she equate the man she had believed him to be with the man she had come to know—the man who terrified her, yet at the same time aroused this need to touch him, hold him, worship him . . . ?

*　　*　　*

She must have dropped off without realising it, but something had disturbed her, because suddenly she was fully awake.

Everything still looked peaceful outside. There were fewer lights now around the lakeside, which told her how late it was. Or early, she thought with a grimace, about to shed the clothes that she was still wearing and take herself off to bed when it came again. The deep, anguished sound of someone in despair—or was it terror? And because she had heard it through the open window it could only have come from the one other occupied room facing the same direction as hers. Paolo's!

She didn't stop to question whether or not she was doing the right thing. Something was wrong. And with Paolo! Fortified by her newly acknowledged love for him, she didn't even consider the chance of any possible danger to herself.

At first all was quiet on the landing. Only the classical figure of a nymph watched silently from its shadowy recess above the stairs. Then it came again. A shout, followed by a series of muffled groans.

Dear heaven! What could be wrong to make a man cry out like that?

She tiptoed barefoot along the landing to his room, and waited, her hand on the doorknob, listening, her heart beating furiously.

The sounds were broken, deep, intermittent groans. Then there was another shout, and so loud now that she wondered why no one else had been disturbed, half expecting a light to snap on on another landing, someone to appear on the stairs, but no one did.

Quietly, Chelsea turned the handle.

Paolo was tossing and turning in his bed, muttering incoherent ramblings in Italian. A thin sheet, his only covering, had somehow become entwined around him, virtually binding him in his restless slumber as he thrashed and twisted about on the wide bed.

'Paolo.' Her diffident whisper did nothing to stir him, only producing another deep groan through the darkness, making her jump. 'Paolo?' The last thing he had said to her was 'Sleep well.' But what devils were driving him for his dreams to be so plagued? she wondered, advancing towards the bed. 'Paolo, wake up! Wake up. You're only dreaming.'

The shoulder beneath the light touch of her hand shuddered convulsively. His skin felt hot and damp. 'Wake up. Wake up, Paolo.' She shook him gently. 'It's all right. It's only a dream.'

He sat up with a violence that scared her, made her pull back from him as a deep sound issued from his throat. He was fighting the restrictions of the sheet, tearing it from his upper torso as if he were fighting some fiend, groaning and gasping now. But at least he was fully awake.

'Where the devil am I? What are you doing here?' His questions, in Italian, seemed to be wrenched from him, but Chelsea understood enough to grasp the gist.

'You were dreaming. A nightmare,' she uttered, feeling as shaken as he sounded. 'It was terrible. I thought you were being murdered.'

In the dim light of one lamp still burning in the garden, she saw his mouth pull down in a barely humorous line. 'So, like a ministering angel, you came to my rescue?'

Was he mocking her or reprimanding her for being there? 'No. I mean . . . I couldn't sleep. I heard you shout . . .' And that, with the fact that she was still fully dressed, would only tell him how disturbed her own thoughts had been, she realised hopelessly, and knew what conclusions he would easily draw from that. He looked as hot as he'd felt, though—hot and unusually discomposed. Even in this light she could see the perspiration glistening on his forehead and bare chest. 'Are you all right?' she ventured tentatively, concerned.

'Perfectly.'

He didn't look it, though, and Chelsea foraged through her mind, looking for similarities, some connection. That journey to Como, today in that lift, the flights of stairs he'd made her climb . . .

And then it clicked, like a faulty mechanism that had just been given one almighty kick into order.

Unconsciously, her fingers strayed over those muscular biceps that had been restricted by the sheet and she whispered, 'You . . . you don't like being confined, do you?'

A cynical sound erupted from him. 'What are you now? Some sort of psychoanalyst?'

Hurt by his derisive tone, and startlingly conscious suddenly of being there in his room, she was about to withdraw, leave him to his own terrifying experiences—but he had other ideas.

'I'm sorry.' He reached out, caught her hand, that barely accented voice velvety soft. 'I'm being a swine, and here you are concerned for my welfare. Take it as a direct result of the dream.'

'A nightmare, you mean,' she corrected him, tremulously, despite her droll smile, because he hadn't released her but was inviting her to sit beside him on the bed. 'What were you dreaming about, anyway?' The mattress depressed slightly under her slender figure as nervously she obeyed.

More relaxed now, Paolo leaned back on an elbow. 'It doesn't matter any more. Much more relevant—do you always make a point of rushing to a man's room when you think he might be in trouble?'

A fine tension stole through her, tautening the fine lines of her profile. 'I've never heard a man having nightmares before.'

'Probably because you haven't slept with any.'

'Thanks!' she said affectedly, deliberately misinterpreting him.

'You haven't, have you?' he said seriously, back in control again.

'If you think you know—why ask?' she uttered tartly, and made to get up.

Quickly, though, he was sitting up, his hands on her shoulders pressing her gently back down onto the bed. His

fingers were warm, dangerously sensual through her thin
blouse.

'I ask because I cannot believe that any man would go
as far as wanting to make you his for life and still be able
to keep his hands off you.' Those warm fingers slid ca-
ressingly down her bare arms, caught her left hand, stroking
idly along her third finger to the pale circle of flesh that
betrayed where her ring had been. 'But now you're free.'

Chelsea's heartbeat seemed suspended beneath an ocean
of sensation. And, as if realising, Paolo laughed, lifting
two fingers to her lips.

Chelsea sucked in her breath, averting her eyes to eschew
the need to wallow in the sight of his semi-nakedness—
those magnificent shoulders, that scarred chest that she
wanted to press her lips against, the hard, tight contours
of his waist.

'And you've come to me.' He lifted her hand, turning it
over, and, tilting his head, let his teeth graze along the sensitive underside of her wrist.

'No.' It was a small, desperate denial, strangled by the
traitorous sensations playing over the periphery of her
nerves.

'Are you saying you weren't thinking about this when
you doused yourself with the perfume you swore you would
never wear?'

Of course. The perfume . . .!

'I didn't douse myself in it,' she said lamely, because it
was all she could think of to say.

'Maybe not, but you weren't wearing it earlier.'

Was he really that aware of her? Even knowing the
perfume she wore—or rather, didn't wear?

'What woman uses perfume before she goes to bed unless
she's expecting to visit—or be visited by—her lover?'

One hand was cradling her head, those strong fingers
buried in her hair's golden softness, and she drew in a breath
as his lips brushed her ear, her cheek, the delicate curve of
her jaw.

'I didn't . . .' she started to protest, but it wasn't even convincing now. She could smell the erotic animal musk rising up from him with his body heat—a potent, masculine scent that had her heart hammering in excitement and fear—fear of the unknown—and nervously she murmured, 'You aren't my lover.'

He laughed softly, his breath a sensual caress as his lips lightly touched the other side of her jaw, the corner of her mouth. 'Not yet, *cara*,' he whispered. 'Not yet.'

Then *when*? This couldn't be her thinking, this—this wanton, abandoned creature, she thought, breathing irregularly because, without her realising it was happening, his chaste kisses had become more of a turn-on than she could ever have imagined possible.

Crazy for the fulfilment of his kiss, she turned her head, desperately seeking his mouth, but as quickly he moved to tease the other corner of hers, tormenting, arousing, deliberately denying her.

'Bastard.'

He laughed again, softly, at her involuntary little oath. 'Are you one of those profane creatures who utters obscenities when she's making love?'

Her heart fluttered inside her. 'Are we making love?'

His lips were nipping her ear-lobe. 'What do you think?'

She couldn't think, only answer with a small murmur of wanting, and as her back arched instinctively, bringing her into even closer contact with him, she heard him catch his breath.

'Do you know what you're doing?' It sounded like a soft admonishment.

'Yes.' It was a meek, enfeebled response.

He chuckled. A low, sexy sound. 'No, *amore*.' His own breath seemed to tremble through him. 'I don't think you do.'

She started to say something—she didn't even know what it was, only that the lips that had been hovering above hers suddenly came down hard over her mouth, crushing her mindless words beneath the shattering reality of his kiss.

Like a wild thing she brought her hands up to grasp his shoulders, greedily seeking the devouring thrust of his tongue with hers. Her body swaying towards him, she heard him groan deep in his throat, uttering through a breathless frenzy of desire her own cry of need as he caught her roughly, possessively against his hard, warm nakedness.

'*Dio buono!* Why did you have to come in here?' There was an angry passion in his voice, a thrilling rebuke that she didn't wholly understand as she moved against him, helping him now as he tugged off the confining barrier of her blouse and trousers, deftly unhooked the lacy bra, dropping them, with little regard, to the floor.

'Paolo...' She knew her figure was good. Her breasts were high and firm and her waist tiny. But compared with the dazzling women who moved in his world she wasn't sure she could compete, and she felt suddenly self-conscious, unsure, shy.

'You're beautiful,' he whispered, as if he knew.

She smiled, her hair spread against his pillows, her eyes slumbrous.

'Not half as beautiful as you are,' she murmured as he knelt above her, her fingers tracing the pale, intriguing scar above his chest.

Her breasts were aching for his caress but he didn't touch her immediately, only bending to allow his teeth to nip the sensitive skin of her throat. Lifting his head, he watched the way her eyes closed, smiled as she groaned her appreciation, and then very gently he slid his arms under her and drew her towards him, just close enough to feel the taut peaks of her breasts harden and thrust against the deep bronze velvet of his chest.

His body hair rasped against the sensitive, swollen globes, creating an almost unbearable need way down in the heart of her femininity.

Driven by desire, she reached up and caught the thick hair at the nape of his neck, pulling his head down, her body language patent and unequivocal as she strained to offer him one throbbing, rosy-tipped breast.

Not needing any further persuasion, he pushed her back onto the bed, looming above her like some unashamed and naked god as his hands claimed the sweet prize of her beautiful breasts.

She sobbed aloud, moving uninhibitedly as his rough palms kneaded their aching fullness, wondering if she would die from pleasure when his thumbs brushed lightly over their hardened tips, teasing, torturing her before he bent to draw one nipple into his mouth.

A surge of heat coursed through her from the fulfilment of his warm mouth. But suddenly she wanted more. Much more . . .

This, then, was what it was like, she thought—the ultimate surrender, the moment when nothing would do but that pinnacle of pleasure, the glory of giving yourself up to the man you loved. Because she needed him now, the sheer power of him inside of her. But she wanted to please him too . . .

She struggled from under him, raising herself up to press her lips against the heated flesh of his throat, kissing him, tasting him. His skin was damp and slightly salty as her tongue ran over the slope of his shoulder, over the rather bumpy texture of his scar.

'Where did you get it—this scar?' she whispered, loving it because it was part of him, part of everything she adored and worshipped about him.

'It was an accident. I've had it years.' He was too imparadised by what she was doing to him to expand upon it, she realised, warmed by her own ability to arouse him as her tongue strayed down his breastbone, her lips nipping at the coarse hair covering his chest. Her hands meanwhile were making a journey of their own, down the warm smoothness of his flanks to his waist and the taut muscles of his abdomen.

'You're perfect,' she whispered, feeling him tense, hearing him groan and watching his eyes close against the pleasure as she touched him in the most intimate way.

'And you have the touch of an angel,' he breathed shudderingly, as though it was too exquisite to take, pushing her back against the pillows after a few hedonistic moments so that he could feel and taste and caress her satin softness, unimpeded by the pleasure that had held him captive to her fondling.

Only the barrier of her oyster silk briefs separated her from him, and their sweat-dampened skin mingled and clung. She sucked in her breath, feeling his lips travelling down her body, his hands constantly following where his mouth had been, massaging, caressing, adoring.

A guttural sound escaped her as the warmth of his mouth burned against the silk of her briefs, exploring the last intimate secret of her body.

Dear heaven! She had never known it could be like this.

'Oh, Paolo, don't stop. Please don't stop.' What sorcery did he weave that he could reduce her to such a helpless victim of her senses? 'Oh, Paolo, love me. Please love me.'

She had never dreamed for one moment that he wouldn't. When he, therefore, moved to sit up, dragging in a breath as though he were battling against the very devil, Chelsea gazed up at him, half-dazed, her face flushed, her forehead creasing with bewilderment.

'What is it?' She could barely draw the breath through her own lungs to speak. 'What's wrong? Why have you stopped?' She reached out, touched his arm. 'Paolo...'

'No.' His voice was firm and decisive.

'No?' She couldn't believe, comprehend what he was saying. 'Why not? I thought... I mean... You can't...'

She couldn't even say it. Frustration was a physical pain, way, way down inside. What had he been doing? Seeing how long it would take him to get her to surrender to him? She couldn't believe that, and from the tautness of his features it was obvious that it was affecting him as profoundly to deny her.

'Why?' was all she could manage on a tormented sob.

'Because a girl like you needs—deserves it all. And I'm not offering what Julian Rendell was offering.' His words were cruel, hitting home hard, though she hadn't for one moment deluded herself into thinking that he could ever love her.

'I realise that,' she said breathlessly, meekly.

'You mean you'd give yourself to me—surrender something you even denied your own fiancé?'

She swallowed. What could she say to that without telling him the truth?

Fortunately, though, he didn't pursue that point; instead he asked, 'And had you given any thought to contraception?'

'No.' It was a small, thin negation, because she had been taking the contraceptive pill when she had been about to embark upon her marriage—marriage to another man— and she'd abandoned it almost immediately after coming here, so perhaps—deep down—she'd realised even then. 'I imagined that you...'

He gave a low chuckle in his throat as he got up, tall and magnificent in his nakedness. 'You think I'm such a...' he paused, searching for a translation '...a stud that you automatically assume I keep a full stock in case one of my female guests accidentally drops into my bed?' He sounded amused, almost tender. 'I'm flattered. But I'm not prepared to take what you're offering—not at this stage. Not until I'm sure you really know what you want.'

But he had—or almost, she thought, his remarkable control torturing her. She was paralysed by desire, too racked by frustration to find the will even to move.

'Oh, Paolo...' She pressed her eyelids tight against the need that was almost unbearable, his name a plea on her lips. 'Please don't leave me like this...'

He had shrugged into a robe. Obviously it was his intention to leave her. Suddenly, though, he came back to her, down to her, and even in the darkness she could see that his lids were weighed down with desire, the stark contours of his face hardened by a passion he was doing his utmost to keep in check.

'My sweet Chelsea... you stretch me to the limit.'

His mouth over hers was like sustenance after star-vation—necessary to her survival, bringing her straining to-wards him with unashamed greed.

She needed him. Oh, God... His hands moulding her nakedness after their cruel deprival were more inflaming than before, her response to his kiss more desperate, in-tensified by the hard passion she provoked as she moved convulsively against him. She wanted fulfilment. Release from this torturous wanting...

Sobbing with need, she clutched at him, her nails sinking tensely into the towelling-covered hardness of his shoulder, spasms shuddering through her as his warm hand moved from her tumescent breasts to the soft plane of her abdomen, then lower, and lower... And pressed down—hard.

Waves of sensation coalesced, one upon the other, the carefully calculated pressure starting a fire inside her—a pulsing, throbbing candescence deep in her loins.

She felt it build, a white, intense heat that spread along her thighs and, as he cupped her, through the aching bud of her femininity. She cried aloud, bringing her legs up to trap his sinewy wrist as she was carried away on a sweet tide of pleasure, collapsing beneath the gasping, sobbing climax that he had made happen for her.

When it was over she turned her face into his chest, breathing the damp musk of his skin, feeling relaxed and, strangely, a little embarrassed.

'What about you?' she managed to ask tremulously at length. His frustration must have been as great. Perhaps it was worse for a man.

'I think you'd better go back to your room.' That shud-dering comment revealed the extent of the restraint that he was having to exercise.

'But you...' Clutching the sheet to her, like Eve sud-denly conscious of her nakedness, she watched as he moved away from her; she got up, feeling diffident and awkward herself, not sure what to say.

'I'm all right.' He sounded slightly impatient with her now, but more controlled nevertheless.

He was standing by the window, that one light in the garden revealing the proud, chiselled lines of his bone structure. A soft pattering outside told her that they were in for another showery night.

'Exactly why did you come in here, Chelsea?' He turned to look at her. She could feel his probing scrutiny even though his face was obscured by shadows.

'I told you,' she said, holding the sheet to her as she wriggled off the bed. 'You were crying out as if the hounds of hell were after you.'

'Ah, yes.' He gave her a wan smile. 'But you stayed.'

Her throat worked nervously before she reached down for her clothes that had been so carelessly discarded. 'You didn't make it very easy for me to leave,' she uttered truthfully, straightening up.

He smiled rather wryly at that. 'And Julian? Didn't he ever make it hard for you to leave him?'

So he was still wondering about that.

'I was never in love with Julian,' she confessed. 'I don't think I ever could have been. That's why I never ... why we ...'

'Didn't ever make love?' There was a pregnant pause. And then he said, 'Is that what this was all about, Chelsea?' He jerked his chin towards the bed. 'Are you saying you're in love with me?'

Of course, he had had her begging him to love her, she thought as she fastened her bra, realising that she had as good as admitted just how deeply she cared about him with that reckless outburst, knowing that he didn't feel anywhere near the same degree of emotion towards her.

'No. I—I don't know,' she faltered, trying to rectify her mistake as convincingly as she could, though it was hard to lie.

She couldn't see his expression because he had turned his back fully on the window, but he must have mistaken that reserve in her voice for something else, because he said,

'It's all right. It's only natural for a girl who has only ever known one boyfriend—' that was a guess because she hadn't actually told him that '—to wonder what it would be like with someone else.'

Is that what he thought?

Fastening the zipper of her trousers, pulling on her blouse, she could only say honestly, 'It was spectacular.'

He leaned back against the wide sill, his arms folded. 'You don't know yet.'

Yet? With her heart jumping in her breast she looked up, met those exciting, shadowy features.

Of course. He intended them to become lovers—in the true sense of the word. But he wouldn't rush her. He wanted her unconditionally—willing, and without any regrets.

'No. No, I don't,' she uttered, wondering through the blindness of her feelings for him if she could ever make him love her. And she knew that that was the first step to disaster as, with a dull ache overshadowing the brief, wild pleasure that he had given her, she whispered, 'Goodnight, Paolo,' and moved swiftly back to her own room.

The lake had never appeared so clear, or the mountains so beautiful, Chelsea thought wistfully, coming out onto the terrace into the bright morning and returning Sophia's equally bright greeting.

Covertly she noted the abandoned chair, the used coffee-cup and plate. So Paolo had already breakfasted, she thought with a clutch of tension in her stomach as she visualised him sitting there reaching for a croissant, the breeze teasing the grey-streaked ebony of his hair.

'You were late rising this morning, Chelsea. You also look a little pale. You are not sickening for anything, I hope?'

Sophia's astute observation was more than a little disconcerting.

'No, I—I don't think so.' She attempted to sound cheerful, even though she was feeling anything but light-hearted this morning. 'I think it must be all this lake-land air!'

Sophia smiled. 'It is the privilege of youth—sleeping in the morning. However, I believe Paolo had a rather restless night.'

'Oh?' Reaching for the silver coffee-pot, Chelsea felt herself flushing.

'Sometimes he is prone to…nightmares,' his mother told her, searching for and finding the right word. 'I thought I heard him call out last night. I came down, but he had quietened by then. I hope you were not disturbed.'

'No,' Chelsea said quickly, and, looking up, hastily averted her eyes. Had Sophia heard her go to her son's room? Heard the tell-tale sounds of what had transpired? Those inscrutable, all-seeing dark eyes—so like Paolo's— gave no indication of what the woman was thinking.

'The nightmares—' she hadn't realised that they were an on-going thing '—is it because he's claustrophobic? Because he is, isn't he?' she prompted, needing to know.

A wan smile touched his mother's lips. 'You're very observant.' Again that keen, assessing scrutiny.

No, just in love with him, Chelsea admitted silently before her hostess went on, 'He hides it too well for most people to notice, and it is not a thing to which he easily admits. He is too proud—too strong to admit to any weakness.'

'Having a phobia isn't necessarily a weakness,' Chelsea stated understandingly, her heart aching for him. But she couldn't let it ache, couldn't let anything sway her from the decision that she had made while she had still been in bed that morning. 'Did something cause it?' To have produced horror in a man like Paolo it must have been something terrifying. And because she had been wondering ever since last night she asked, 'Does it have anything to do with that scar?'

'His scar?'

Chelsea felt her colour deepen, recalling the way that raised flesh had felt against her lips. 'Yes.'

'Have you asked him?'

She swallowed, nodded. 'Mmm.' She could hardly tell Sophia how her tentative query had been forgotten in the mind-blowing rapture of their lovemaking.

'And he didn't tell you?' Sophia sent a glance lakewards, to where the small white pyramid of a sailing boat was moving gracefully across the blue water. 'Perhaps he prefers to forget about it, in which case I suggest that you let him, *mia cara*. Paolo can be very... what is the word?... close, I think you say. And if my son doesn't want to do something—he doesn't do it. I am afraid he has inherited my habit—and his father's—of being totally obstinate, immovable when he wants to be. Unlike Giorgio who was often the opposite—far too complaisant...'

The woman glanced down at her plate, her eyelids heavy. Doubtless, the tragedy of her elder son's death would remain eternally painful. Chelsea sympathised, wondering if it had been that complaisance of Giorgio Rossetti's that had kept him from seeing when something was threatening his marriage, and her thoughts strayed unhappily to Neil.

How had he felt, her cousin, falling in love with a woman who wasn't free to return his love? How must he have felt when her distraught husband had plunged his car over that cliff? For the first time she really considered the anguish that Neil must have suffered with such a burden of guilt to carry. But had it brought him some happiness, that brief, illicit love affair? Or had it left him as mixed up and confused as she was feeling now?

'I thought he was over them—the nightmares.' The woman gave a sigh of resignation. 'I am unhappy to say, *cara*, I do not think your being here has helped in that respect.'

'My being—?' Chelsea broke off, frowning. Of course. She was too much a reminder of the past. And no doubt those restless ghosts, torturing Paolo with the intensity of his hatred for her cousin, would probably be enough to stir up other demons...

A brief silence stretched across the terrace. 'I'm sorry.' Chelsea murmured sadly. 'Anyhow, I'll be leaving today.'

Sophia looked suddenly both shocked and apologetic. 'Oh, *mamma mia*! I did not mean that. The last thing I intended was that you should feel unwelcome . . .'

'No, really, you didn't. I mean I *don't*,' Chelsea stressed, swift to put her hostess at ease. 'I'd already made up my mind.' Because she had, while she was still in bed, having woken up feeling keen excitement as she'd remembered last night, and feeling utterly, thoroughly confused.

Just three weeks ago she had been getting married—married to Julian. And here she was, having suffered one devastating shock after another, ready to plunge headlong into another relationship . . .

She needed time to think, to sort herself out. She loved Paolo—of that at least she was sure. But so much had happened in so short a time; how could she make any rational decisions, commit herself to an ecstatic yet probably very insecure relationship with him, without first giving a good deal of thought to all that it would imply, giving herself a degree of space in which to breathe?

'I'm already packed. I'll be leaving straight after breakfast,' she told Sophia as casually as she was able.

'I'm sorry.' The woman's regret was genuine as she laid her napkin down, having finished breakfast. 'I shall miss you.' Then she added, 'Paolo didn't say anything to me about it this morning. Have you told him?'

With a tightening in her stomach, Chelsea shook her head, stiffening as his deep voice suddenly came across the terrace.

'Told me what?'

Where had he come from? The boathouse?

Chelsea's heart was thudding as her gaze skimmed over his lean, casual elegance, his sheer dynamism causing her heart to somersault, her blood to surge with all the need and want and hunger that his very presence called to life.

'Well?'

With a wry glance in Chelsea's direction, Sophia got up, leaving them to it.

'I'm leaving. Today,' she blurted out bluntly in her haste to get it over and done with. Too bluntly, she realised, seeing the hard puzzlement lining his face.

'Just like that?'

She had to admit that it was rather sudden.

'Don't try and stop me.' It was a small, panicked appeal.

'Oh, don't worry. I wouldn't dream of it.' He sounded grim, sarcastic and understandably wounded. 'What brought this on?'

'Paolo, please. Try to understand...'

'Understand what?' he demanded, following her as she turned away from the house, down into the rose garden. The scent was overwhelming this morning, and moisture from the previous night's rain still clung to the crimson of the less exposed blooms. 'Last night you were prepared to risk getting pregnant to spend the night in my bed. And this morning you're walking out?'

'I'm not walking out.'

He grimaced. 'Then what would you call it?'

She looked across the lake to the spire of some distant church nestling in the mountains.

'I need to go home for a while. I'm just so mixed up...'

'About what?'

My feelings for you, she wanted to say, but she didn't. Perhaps it wasn't even that. Perhaps it was the rightness and wrongness of them. But *he* hadn't mentioned anything last night about feelings when she'd been begging him to take her. But then neither had he been prepared to initiate her into a relationship when he wasn't prepared to make a commitment to her himself.

'Try and put yourself in my shoes,' she adjured, still trying to make him understand. 'Only three weeks ago I was engaged to someone else—'

'And you still haven't got him out of your system, is that it?'

'No!' For heaven's sake, why wasn't he helping her? 'It's just all been too quick. I need time. Air to breathe...'

'And exactly how much time do you need?' His voice was cold. So why did she imagine that there was a note of raw emotion embedded in it? 'Either you want us—here and now—together. Or you don't.'

Exasperated, she turned away, groaning, 'It isn't that easy.'

'Isn't it?'

She gasped as he pulled her round, caught her to him, dragging her head back by a fistful of her hair. His eyes darkened as he watched the way her pupils dilated at the sensations rocking her from the hard warmth of him, and his breathing deepened as he inhaled the erotic fragrance that, strangely, despite her shower, still lingered on her skin.

'Dulcibel-la.' He made it sound like a prelude to sex, not just the name of a wilful teenager whom she had never met. 'You know—at first my production team wanted to call it Imprevedibile—unpredictable. Perhaps I should have let them. You put on an amazing show of wanting me last night.'

Chelsea closed her eyes. 'It wasn't a show.'

'No? Then what was it?'

Oh, God! If only she could say, I love you. And there are too many reasons why I shouldn't!

Instead she said, 'I don't think I want an affair with you, Paolo.' And tentatively she went on, 'Perhaps . . . perhaps you were right last night when you said a girl like me needs it all.' And, hoping he would release her, she added, 'Or maybe I do just need to get Julian out of my system before . . . before embarking on a relationship with someone else. It wouldn't be fair . . . to either of us . . .'

'To either of us?' His laugh was harsh. 'So that's that, then, is it? *Finito!*'

The fingers gripping her shoulders hurt, and the intensity of emotion that darkened his features as he bent his head almost made her sag against him, but rational thinking pre-

vailed in time. If he kissed her, she knew she'd be hopelessly his, and it was only desire on his part, after all.

'This just confuses me—and I don't want that,' she protested breathlessly, and, pulling free, tore away from him
before he could say another word.

CHAPTER NINE

CHELSEA watched the flock of pigeons soar over the little Hampstead garden, careful not to spill the tea she was carrying down to her father, who was cleaning out their loft.

'That's my lass.' He beamed as he emerged from the little wooden structure and saw her coming down the path. 'Tell your mother I won't be too long.' Amazingly, in the past month, her parents had decided to live together again. She wasn't convinced that it would work, but she was happy at least that they were giving it another try.

'You should stay out here in the fresh air. Put some colour back into those cheeks of yours,' Rupert Adamson recommended as Chelsea turned to go back inside. 'I know it was a shock to you—finding out the lad you were marrying was...corrupt.' His unusually mild description of her ex-fiancé caused Chelsea to pull a wry face. 'But you can't mope around for ever because of it. You've not been yourself since you came back.'

'I'm *not* moping about it, Dad,' she stressed, going back across the stepping-stone path set in the lawn. How could she tell him that it wasn't her breakup with Julian that was making her unhappy, that it was simply that her heart was aching for another man—a man whom, she realised, she would probably never see again?

It had been nearly three months now since her hasty departure from Lombardy. But though she had waited, hoped, prayed even for some communication from Paolo—and foolishly, she told herself, because hadn't she been the one to reject what he had been offering?—each day had brought only disappointment, cutting and intense.

* * *

October heralded a month that was windy and wet, and only added to her disconsolation.

One lunchtime she bought a bottle of Dulcibella just to torture herself—and spent the rest of the day and a long, sleepless night tormented by the erotic memories that the fragrance induced.

She kept her mind on her job, just. She simply lost her bounce and sparkle, along with her appetite, and if anyone noticed then they didn't mention it. Word had obviously circulated of how she had been abandoned on her wedding day. A few of her close colleagues had been at the church, knew she'd flown out to Milan to join Julian—who, she had told them, had encountered some professional difficulties, although she hadn't been specific. And if they wondered why she was no longer wearing her ring, then no one asked her directly, for which she was immensely relieved.

One day when she was dealing with documents for a client in Como she had to fight back tears, wondering why the pain of her loss was getting worse by the day instead of better. But she knew the answer to that. If she hadn't fought against her feelings for Paolo, had accepted him on his terms, she could have been deep in the heart of a full-blown relationship with him now. She only knew that if she'd had the chance again, then nothing would have stood in her way. No matter how inadvisable it might have been, or how she might have had to suffer when he'd finally cut her out of his life—as he would have eventually—nothing could have been more torturous than what she was going through now, she thought, grieving for the brief happiness she might have had with him.

She didn't notice the office junior come in, or how flushed and excited the girl looked, until she said, 'Chelsea...you've got a visitor in Reception! I know your ex was involved with one or two illustrious names, but I didn't know *you* were! I mean...*Rossetti*?'

Fortunately the girl was so excited that she didn't seem to notice how shocked Chelsea looked. Nor could she tell how her heart was suddenly hammering, or how her legs had gone so weak that she was wondering how she was ever going to make it down to the company's plush reception area, but somehow she did.

'Chelsea? Chelsea Adamson?'

Her disappointment was so overwhelming that it was an effort to conceal it from the slim young girl who had just stood up and was coming towards her.

'Yes.' This beautiful girl who radiated chic with her long black hair and her rust silk suit wasn't the person she'd imagined, ached to see. 'And you are . . .?' Good heavens, why couldn't she stop her voice from shaking?

'Throw me out if you want to.' The girl looked suddenly belligerent, as though Chelsea might be about to do just that. 'I'm Dulcibella. Dulcibella Rossetti.'

'Oh?' What was she doing here? Chelsea couldn't think straight, not even to notice that the girl's English was every bit as fluent as her uncle's. 'Paolo?' she uttered quickly as the notion hit her. 'Is he . . . all right?'

Dulcibella seemed to relax. She even laughed a little nervously. 'Oh, he's in great shape—as always. But I think he'd skin me if he knew I had called to see you. When I suggested it to him he strongly forbade me even to ring you.'

'Oh?' A deep ache made itself felt beneath Chelsea's ribcage. Why would he do that? Unless . . .

'Look . . .' Dulcibella cast a disconcerted look around the busy, open reception area. 'Do you think we could go somewhere more private to talk?'

Chelsea was only too glad to. She couldn't understand why Paolo's niece was here.

'I—I came because . . . well, because I gather that you and Julian Rendell didn't marry after all,' she explained when they were sitting in the small room next to the main entrance. 'And, for what it's worth, I wanted to say I was sorry you broke up. Although my uncle says it wasn't, I know it was all my fault.'

If she'd told Paolo that, then perhaps that was why he had forbidden this visit, Chelsea reasoned distractedly. He knew the more serious consequences that had caused her and Julian to part.

'I was selfish,' the girl continued openly. 'I was hurt and angry. When I discovered Julian was Signor Adamson's friend—that *you* were actually his cousin—'

'Your uncle told you that?' Chelsea, surprised, couldn't help interjecting.

Dulcibella's black hair moved like satin as she shook her head. 'No, he would not divulge anything so confidential to me. He would have known how I would probably have reacted. I discovered it quite by accident—from some papers I'd mistakenly picked up that were lying on his desk in his apartment. But when I knew, I wanted to hurt you both. To get back at Signor Adamson in some way through you for what he did to my parents. I know it was wrong, but that's why I made up that dreadful story when I thought I was pregnant. I wanted someone to pay for what happened to my father—and for what almost happened to my uncle too.'

Chelsea could almost feel the pain pent up inside the seventeen-year-old. And as it registered, she stressed, puzzled, 'Your uncle? *Paolo?*'

'Yes, Paolo.' The girl's chin stuck out in proud defiance as she spoke his name. 'He doesn't give in when I shout and scream, or pander to me like everyone else does—unless he thinks it is best for me—and for that I love and respect him very much. I was only twelve when...when my mother left and...my father had that...*accident.*' Her tone implied that she knew it was more than that.

'To get me away from it all Uncle Paolo took me skiing. Stefano Verde, the sculptor—he's my uncle's friend—and his wife, they came with us. One morning Signora Verde and I stayed back at the lodge, and Signor Adamson called looking for my uncle. He'd been drinking and he looked so...angry. He was shouting something about Uncle Paolo stealing everything from him—that he was going to get even with him.

'I wanted Signora Verde to take me up to where he was skiing and warn him, but she wouldn't because my uncle had instructed her to keep me in because of the changeable weather conditions that day. Signor Verde—he doesn't have my uncle's stamina—returned first. I told him about Signor Adamson but he said that it was nothing my uncle couldn't handle.

'Then news of the avalanche came. We waited, but he didn't come back. All that day until nearly dark I thought he was dead—until someone came and told us he'd been taken to the hospital, and I knew then that the reason he hadn't come back was to do with meeting your cousin. My uncle was injured as well as badly frostbitten, but they said he kept muttering Signor Adamson's name and fought against their moving him until he'd made them understand that your cousin had been up there with him.

'They found him totally unharmed—apart from a bruised cheek—under a ledge about a quarter of a mile from where they'd found my uncle. My uncle's hat and one of his skis was close by, under a pile of debris. Broken trees, branches...' Dulcibella gave a little shrug. 'They could only assume he had been trying to take shelter there too and was hit by a jagged branch which caused an awful gash to his shoulder before he was swept down that mountain. He had been buried—conscious under the snow—literally for hours.'

The horror pierced through Chelsea like a cold blade, and with it came a slow awakening to the truth. The bruising that Neil had sustained must have been from where Paolo had hit him. Hit him for his own benefit. Wasn't that what he had said? But what had he done then? Dragged him to safety. A man he had hated—had had every reason to hate. But if that was true then he must have risked his life— nearly sacrificed that life—to save Neil. But Neil hadn't known anything about that because Paolo had hit him— knocked him unconscious to ensure the safety of them both because Neil had been panicking—and Paolo would never have admitted even to her—perhaps especially to her—that act of gallantry towards her cousin.

A sob caught in her throat. Dear heaven! Why had she ever carried on doubting his integrity? Because she had—deep down. And those nightmares he still suffered from, that fear of being trapped... The horror of that day still plagued him in an almost paralysing phobia.

Oh, Paolo! she thought achingly, wanting to be with him, to share the mental pains that lurked behind that hard outer shell.

She didn't realise the intensity of emotion revealing itself until Dulcibella whispered incredulously, '*Santo cielo!* Are you in love with him too?'

Too? Jealousy stabbed at her as she remembered Elena Lisi. 'No, I...' What was the point of denying it? she thought despairingly. Instead she shrugged, tried to smile as she said, 'He's a very attractive man.'

'Don't I know it!' Dulcibella grimaced. 'You wouldn't believe that every one of my friends has at some time tried to make him... interested, and naturally he's only amused by it. But I can't understand it—I mean, he's so *old*!'

And you, Chelsea thought, unable to contain a wry smile at this as she considered the five-year gap in their ages which might as well have been ten, are so young.

'Anyway,' Dulcibella was continuing, 'he's finally made me see that my mother must have been as willing to have that affair with Signor Adamson as he was with her or it could never have happened—and I know that couldn't have been easy for him. After all, it wasn't just my father that he saw destroy himself—it was his brother too. But you won't tell him I came here, will you?' Suddenly her fine, beautiful features were etched with tension. 'We'll only have a terrific argument,' she stated with a roll of eyes, 'which he'll win, as always.'

'Is he here—in London with you?'

How could Dulcibella appreciate how it made her heart thump to ask that simple question? Or how viciously it tore through her as the younger girl supplied the answer? 'He was. He had business here for a few days, but this morning he flew back to Milan.'

And that was that, Chelsea thought. That said it all. More than his niece turning up and apologising for her behaviour, more than Dulcibella's innocent revelation about the way he had saved her cousin, that simple statement speared and wounded her more than it had been possible for her to imagine she could be hurt.

He had been in London and hadn't come to see her. So what did that tell her? Only that he wasn't interested. And his forbidding Dulcibella to see her? Couldn't the reason for that simply be because he didn't want anything to do with her himself?

Pain settled on Chelsea after Dulcibella had gone—a heart-lacerating misery that even giving in to tears couldn't ease, although she tried. God, how she tried!

Eventually, when the first few nights had passed, a cold, numbing acceptance took its place. She wrote to Neil, explaining in the most delicate terms that she now appreciated the full extent of the trauma he must have suffered five years ago, the facts of which the family had taken great pains to protect her from. With all the strength of her love for both him and Paolo, she put to her cousin that he had been wrong about Paolo Rossetti, stating briefly the facts as Dulcibella had given them to her while trying to keep any indication of her own hopeless love for the man out of the letter.

She was relieved, therefore, when a little under two weeks later she received a rather reserved but friendly enough response from him, stating that there had been faults on both sides but that now it was all in the past. He finished by wishing her well, though strangely expressed little regret over her broken relationship with Julian.

Perhaps Neil, also, had realised how unsuited they were, she thought, shuddering as she read his letter again, before coming out of the office that evening into the murky drizzle of the chilly autumn evening. If Dulcibella hadn't made up that story about Julian being the father of her child—and

Paolo hadn't suspected him enough to drag him over to Italy...

She shivered again as she reached the bus stop, turning up the collar of her raincoat. Perhaps she had something to thank Dulcibella for, after all. On the other hand, she thought as she was jostled and pushed by others trying to get onto the bus that had just pulled up, if she'd never gone to Italy in the first place, never met Paolo Rossetti, she wouldn't have fallen in love with him and be suffering this torturous regret and loneliness that she was suffering now.

Finding a seat on one of the benches facing across the bus, she stared sightlessly at the blur of neons and car lamps through the grimy, misted glass.

'Fares, please.' The portly conductor was pushing his way past the people standing in the aisle, and automatically Chelsea flashed her pass at him, putting it away to gaze distractedly along the bus. And suddenly every cell seemed to freeze.

A man sat halfway down the bus, in an expensive-looking dark raincoat over a dark suit and immaculate white shirt, and there was no mistaking the silver-streaked temples and the achingly familiar lift of that arrogant head.

She glanced quickly away, her mouth dry, her heart racing. How could it be Paolo, millionaire magnate, sitting there in the heart of the rush hour, on a London bus?

She ventured another look at him, her eyes linking with his, too shocked, too surprised even to smile. He hadn't contacted her, had he? Not in more than three months. Hadn't even bothered when he'd been in England before. So what right did he have to imagine she owed him any sense of recognition?

Too stunned to do anything but stare unsmilingly at him, for a moment she thought he looked about to get up. He shot a glance up at the crowded aisle and then obviously thought better of trying to force his way past that oppressive wall of bodies. The bus seemed claustrophobic even to her. For fleeting seconds she saw the tension locking the muscles of his face, the struggle—hard won—as the conductor pushed his way up to him and asked for his fare.

'I wanta Chelsea.'

Her breathing stilled, every nerve leaping from its torpid state just at hearing the rich, deep timbre of his voice. But what on earth was he saying?

'Sorry, guv'nor. We don't go to Chelsea.' The conductor sounded decidedly irate.

'But I want-a Chelsea. See. I pay! How much?' He was holding out a handful of coins, gabbling away in Italian and broken English with all the gestures to match, sounding more like some over-adventurous phrase-book tourist rather than a Cambridge graduate who knew the language probably better than she did.

But he was drawing the attention of everyone on the bus, including her! Chelsea thought, mortified, and realised through her heart-thumping discomfiture that this was her penalty for ignoring him. And, as if that weren't enough, he was looking straight at her now and saying something slowly and more seriously for her to understand, and though her Italian was far from fluent she grasped the gist of what he was telling her—that if she didn't get up out of her seat now he was coming over there and giving her a passionate, no-holds-barred, Italian kiss!

He would too!

Mindful of his disregard for convention, she jumped up fearfully. She hadn't forgotten his uninhibited passion that day at Tremezzo!

'It's all right, conductor! I know this man.' Somehow she managed to squeeze her way through the busful of curious spectators and, with her brown eyes indignant, though her heart was racing, she said in Italian, hoping she was getting it right, 'I'll get you for this,' and smiled for the benefit of the other passengers. And with mock sweetness she added to the conductor, 'I'll be happy to tell him where to go.'

Paolo looked no less than amused, and as the conductor rang the bell to stop the bus, muttering something about foreigners, he followed Chelsea off into the spitting rain.

'Your Italian's as bad as he thought my English was!' he laughed, exuding that dangerous charm as he steered her out of the road and onto the safety of the pavement. Even the casual nearness of him sent fire licking along her veins.

'What was I supposed to do—with you showing me up like that? What was the point of it?' she challenged him testily.

'The point of it?' He looked at her as though she shouldn't need to ask. 'I had to get you off that bus somehow.'

'Why?' she queried, and it sounded like a sob. Beside them a car horn blasted, lights flashed, a sea of changing colour reflected on the wet road. 'What were you doing on there anyway?'

She hadn't realised how censorious she sounded until he laughed and said, 'It's public transport. I didn't realise that excluded Italian citizens.' And when his flippant remark drew the briefest smile from her he stated solemnly, 'As a matter of fact I was following you.'

'Why?' She glanced across the space that separated them and wished she hadn't. Just the familiar twitch of his mouth, the hard excitement of his features made her senses quiver, robbed her of her ability to think. 'Why couldn't you have telephoned? Or called—like any normal human being? You know where I live.'

'And work,' he supplied, reminding her of his thorough investigation of her when she had been going out with Julian. 'I did call at your office, or rather, I tried to—this evening. I saw you walk out when I was on the other side of the street. After risking life and limb crossing that road, I'd nearly caught up with you when you hopped onto that bus—and then when you looked at me as though you didn't want to know—'

'Me?'

He stopped at the same instant as she did—as though they were one.

'I thought you were the one who—' She broke off, afraid of expressing too much, her features pale and tense beneath the dark intensity of his. She couldn't bear it when he looked at her like that, when the flagrant power of his masculinity threatened to consume her, and unable to rein in the emotion that was searing her insides, unthinkingly, on a wave of desperation, she blurted out, 'I thought you'd gone back to Milan!'

His dark brows drew together. After all, how could she have known his movements? And, striding determinedly beside her again, he said quietly, 'Dulcie came to see you, didn't she?'

Agitatedly she looked at him, opened her mouth to exonerate his niece and then turned away, knowing it was useless.

'It's all right,' he consoled her. 'I got it out of her myself.'

She breathed a small sigh of relief. She wouldn't have liked betraying the younger girl's confidence.

'She said you always won,' she murmured with a hint of rebellion.

'If you know that, then why do you continue to fight me, Chelsea? On that bus? Here now? At my villa?'

His reference to that bitter-sweet time with him back in the summer caused a tight, sharp twinge along her breastbone. And then, without waiting for her answer, he was hailing a taxi.

'You'll be lucky...' she started to say, but one was already pulling up at the kerb as though just the snap of his fingers was a royal command.

'Park Lane,' he said, giving the driver the name of his hotel.

'Hampstead,' Chelsea countered, her pulses leaping. If he got her in his hotel she wouldn't have a chance!

'Park Lane.'

'Hampstead.' She'd promised her parents she'd call round this evening.

'Make up your minds.' Fortunately the driver sounded amused as Paolo urged her into the back.

'Park Lane,' he said again, and it was settled.

'Your mother mentioned that you were totally obstinate,' she complained, staring out of the window, refusing to look at him.

He gave a low chuckle. 'You seem to have taken a great deal of interest in discussing me with my family.'

What could she say to that?

'Relax,' he advised smilingly after a moment, as she sent a rather wary glance in his direction. 'I'm not going to take you up to my suite and rip your clothes off as soon as we get inside the door. But I would appreciate being somewhere where we can talk in relative seclusion.'

'Are you visiting?'

Despite her pulses racing from the images his words conjured up, Chelsea noticed the face that Paolo pulled at the driver's untimely intrusion and had to suppress a giggle.

'In a manner of speaking,' she heard him tell the man uncommunicatively. Like her, he didn't want to be talking to anyone else. He just wanted her alone.

'This is the chic part of town, if you don't mind paying the prices.' The small talk washed over her. All she was alive to was Paolo's vital presence beside her, the electrifying nearness of him, the casual brush of his sleeve as his arm accidentally touched hers. 'We've got it all here. Hartnell. Rossetti. Armani... You'll have to hang onto your credit cards, though, if you let your ol' lady loose in this neck of the woods!'

Paolo caught the look of indignation on Chelsea's face and laughed softly down at her. 'I'm afraid my wife doesn't believe in all those designer clothes,' he said, still laughing at her.

'You're lucky! My wife...' The driver plunged into a spiel about his spouse's extravagant shopping sprees—exaggerated for the benefit of tourists, Chelsea felt sure, though she barely took any of it in.

'Your *what*?' she whispered to Paolo, trying to sound nonchalant in spite of what he had just called her.

He brought his arm across the back of her seat, the movement drawing her attention to his hard, lean elegance beneath the raincoat. 'It saves complicated explanations,' was his dry, equally low-voiced response.

Of course. She hardly meant anything so serious to him— this man who had the world's most beautiful women at his feet and his name in lights here at the very pulse of the world. She could see that famous signature now above an exclusive shop, even while her brain was trying to deny what his intimate, masculine cologne was doing to her.

She was subdued when he eventually brought her into the luxurious hotel, and must have looked surprised as he settled her in a quiet corner of the bar.

'If I took you upstairs now we wouldn't talk,' he stated plainly, making her wonder if her love for him made her so transparent. 'And I feel we need to. I've no intention of pressuring you into a relationship you might not want.'

No, he wouldn't. He'd said that back in the summer, she reflected as he wandered over to the bar, envying yet hurting at the way he could talk about a relationship with her so matter-of-factly. There were only a handful of customers there, talking quietly. Beyond the fronds of some exotic, cultivated palms, a pianist played.

'I'm afraid this is as private as it gets.'

'Thanks,' she said when he returned with the glass of grapefruit juice that she had ordered. He was drinking bitter—dark with a smooth, creamy head. 'Why did you want to see me?'

He laughed that soft, disbelieving laugh. 'Do you really need to ask?'

She looked down at the pale liquid in her glass, finding the dark power of his gaze too disturbing. No, she thought. He still wanted her—wanted her as much—heaven help her!—as she still wanted him.

'It's good to see you.'

It sounded so meaningless, so trite. And perhaps he thought so too, because his mouth moved wryly before he said, 'You too.' And then he said, 'You aren't particularly easy to forget.'

Chelsea caught her breath and plucked up courage. 'Nor are you,' she murmured, surprising herself with the almost involuntary admission.

'Well, that's something, anyway.' His gaze caught hers, willed her to look at him. 'I haven't stopped thinking about you since the day you took off like a scared bird.'

'I had to,' she muttered, running her finger absently round the rim of her glass. 'I was so...'

'Confused?' He sounded mildly mocking. 'Wasn't that what you said?'

'I couldn't help the way I *felt*,' she stressed, defending her actions. 'Everything happened so fast...'

'And your conscience wouldn't allow you to get seriously involved with the man who'd left your cousin for dead.'

She had used those very words back in the summer, and now they made her wince. 'I know that isn't true,' she said quickly. But of course *he* hadn't known that she knew. As far as he was concerned, she still doubted him. 'I'm sorry,' she whispered, studying those long dark fingers curved around the glass as he drank. And with a catch in her voice she added, 'I was so wrong about you...'

He could have been angry. She wouldn't have blamed him if he had been, but he wasn't. He merely shrugged again as he put the half-empty glass back on the table. 'We all make mistakes.'

'But mine was unforgivable.' Against the background of soft music her voice was achingly penitent.

'What do you want me to do?' The briefest of smiles touched his mouth. 'Seek reparation?'

'It isn't anything to joke about,' she reproved him, as though only some harsh penance could absolve her from her wildly inaccurate judgement of him. 'When Dulcibella told me how you got that scar—'

'Dulcibella had no right!'

Yes, even Sophia had said he was proud, though she knew now that he was both proud and modest. 'She didn't intend to.' She had to make it clear that the younger girl hadn't deliberately set out to betray his confidences. 'She was merely trying to impress upon me how much she hated "Signor Adamson",' Chelsea mimicked kindly. 'Neil.'

'Yes, I'm afraid that will take some changing.' From the way his chest expanded it was obvious that it wouldn't be easy for him either.

'She's learning to live with it,' she told him gently, and, deciding that he'd probably like to hear it, she said, 'Do you know that she thinks the sun shines out of you?'

His mouth lifted on one side, and she could tell that he was quietly pleased. 'She isn't easy,' he admitted.

Chelsea pulled a face. 'Neither are you.'

'No,' he admitted further. 'I suppose that makes three of us.'

'Me?' She laughed tensely, nervously. 'I *could* take exception to that!'

'But you won't.'

She shook her head, the movement revealing the soft gold highlights in her hair. When he looked at her with such dark penetration she couldn't speak; she just melted, caved in like some weak, insubstantial soufflé.

'Have you heard anything from Julian?' The sudden sobriety of his tone, his expression caused her heart to skip a beat. Why was he asking?

'It's *over*,' she stressed, guessing that that was what he wanted to know.

'Does it still hurt?' He was studying her obliquely.

'No,' she admitted truthfully. 'I just regret having been such a fool—believing in him—trusting him...'

Paolo's mouth tugged at one corner. 'We're all fools to some extent, Chelsea. Particularly over matters of the heart.'

Not you, she thought. You're much too level-headed— far too immune. But she said only, 'I feel mostly for his family—particularly his mother. Mum tells me she's in the process of moving, just in case the neighbours ever find out. She's so pretentious I don't think she'd ever be able to live it down.'

Paolo's smile was distant. 'And what about you?'

She cast a guarded look at him, then glanced down again at the dregs of her juice. 'What about me?' she queried, breathing shallowly.

He pushed his glass aside and leaned forward, elbows on the table, his linked hands supporting his chin. 'Are you happy, *mia cara*?'

Her mouth trembled as she tried to smile. 'Why shouldn't I be?'

'Let me guess.' He was getting slightly impatient with her inclination to answer all his questions with a question. 'Because you need a man in your life who, I suspect, isn't sitting too far away from you at this moment. Because you're still tantalising me with a perfume that smells more erotic on you than on any other woman I've met, and you didn't get it from me because that particular bottle is still where you left it. In which case you must have purchased some, which would suggest to me that you're either very keen to boost my company's profits or you have a rather masochistic tendency to wallow in certain . . . fantasies.'

How clever he was! 'I could just happen to like it,' she suggested hastily.

'You could.' But he knew her better. 'Sweet Chelsea . . .' The way he pronounced her name never failed to turn her bones to liquid, and she held her breath as his hard, long fingers encircled hers, drawing them up to press them to his lips. 'I haven't stopped thinking about these either. The way you touched me . . . The scent of your hair. That exasperating way you have of always wanting the last word. The way you look—move.' He caught her other hand, clasping it with the other, flat together between both of his. 'The way you kiss.'

He dipped his head and his lips sent sensuous messages down both her index fingers, his mouth moist and warm and exceedingly erotic on their sensitive tips.

'Why didn't you come to see me when you were here before?' It was a plaintive, injured little accusation while she wondered how she could avert what was going to happen, what she had feared—for her heart and her sanity's sake—would happen, if ever she saw him again.

'I wanted to—believe me, I wanted to,' he whispered hoarsely. 'But I didn't know how you'd receive me. I wasn't sure if you still felt something for Rendell. Besides, that last day you seemed very adamant about not becoming involved with me—but I was determined to pursue you, to try to change your mind—when the time was right.

'When Dulcie confessed that she had been to see you I was livid at first. And then, instead of the usual rebellious attack about my being unreasonable and old-fashioned and not understanding her, she hurled a few things at me about being blind and only being so angry about her seeing you because I wanted to so much myself.' He gave a wry grimace of acceptance. 'She's a very shrewd little girl.'

'Like her uncle—and not so little.' Chelsea smiled, breathless from the realisation of his determination to pursue her. And he would succeed, would use and imparadise her and then abandon her as brutally as she'd believed he'd abandoned her cousin, and she'd be unable to stop him—because she loved him. And with her heart beating faster she asked, 'What did she mean about you being blind?' Had the other girl told him about this hopeless love that she, Chelsea, harboured for him?

'I think,' he said seductively, caressing one of her smooth palms with a sensuous thumb, 'she could see something only a member of her own sex could see—young though she is—though she didn't actually spell it out to me.' And softly he said, 'Was she right, Chelsea?'

His eyes were mesmerising her and she swallowed, her throat clogging with the intensity of her feelings. 'What do you think?' she murmured, powerless to prevent herself revealing all she wanted him to know.

'Damn you,' he cursed with a soft vehemence, his features rigid, because she had done it again. 'Give me a straight answer for once—at least over this,' he rasped.

God! How could even provoking his anger arouse her? 'You usually swear in Italian,' she teased shyly, the words trembling from her lips. And, seeing that hard demand glittering in his eyes, she whispered, 'Yes,' and dropped her gaze, afraid still of laying her emotions so bare.

His breath came shudderingly from his lungs. 'Then I wasn't wrong.'

No, she thought, meeting his eyes again, oblivious to the music and the chatter and the relaxed ambience of her surroundings. He was more certain of her than she would ever be of him. But what did it matter when he was here—now? When he was looking at her as though all that mattered to him was to take her to his bed and never let her out of it? When she was craving for him to take her in his arms, undress her, to feel his lips on hers and his warm hands caressing her body...?

'Come on.' His soft command broke through her sensual stupor. They got up, leaving their half-finished drinks on the table.

CHAPTER TEN

'I THOUGHT you only used stairs,' Chelsea murmured numbly, when he urged her into a vacant lift. Her head was in a spin, every nerve throbbing with anticipation.

'I can't wait that long,' he breathed hoarsely, his very need fanning the flames of her own desire.

'But your phobia...' The words didn't seem to belong to her as she stood facing him at a respectable distance.

'I'll get over it,' he said tensely, waiting for the doors to close.

She seemed locked in a vacuum, where only the sight and scent and sound of Paolo existed for her. Later she would have to face the reality of pain—of an existence without him. But for now...

'I didn't realise,' she murmured dazedly as the doors began to move, 'that it was because of Neil. That you nearly died because of him...'

His face was a rigid mask. 'Not half as much as I've nearly died, *carissima*, because of you.'

The doors had barely closed before he obliterated the charged space between them, meeting the searching frenzy of her mouth with his as he pulled her back with him against the wall.

His hands were in her hair, holding her head still, urgently seeking the familiar contours of her body as she writhed in wild responses to his searching caresses.

'Oh, *carissima*...' His breathing was as laboured as hers.

It was only desire, she thought. That basic, masculine instinct that toppled empires and lured women into sacrificing everything for one whispered promise of commitment. But she knew she would never have commitment from him, nor did she want to think about it as, gratifyingly, her seeking fingers found the hard rising of his chest beneath his raincoat and his jacket, glorying in the warmth of him through the fine shirt.

Supported by the wall, he had caught her firmly between his thighs, his dark, animal strength thrilling her as he forced her head back, grasping the pale swathe of her hair while his teeth grazed the paler column of her throat with a sensual savagery.

'My God! If I could take you now...' Above the rasp of his need the doors were opening again.

Unable to drag herself from the confines of her desire, Chelsea buried her face in the fine material of his shirt, needing to recover. She could smell his body cologne, feel the tremors shuddering through him, signifying his own battle for control.

'Well, really...' An affronted matron, waiting for the lift with a male companion, was looking disgustedly at them. But they had reached their floor and numbly Chelsea allowed Paolo to guide her out.

'You should try it some time, *signora*,' he sent back smugly over his shoulder. 'They say it's even better going down.'

His outrageous remark drew a tremulous giggle from Chelsea as the lift whined mercifully away.

'You're such an exhibitionist!' She exhaled, her voice feeble with desire. 'Unconventional!' Wasn't that one of the reasons she loved him, why he excited her? she thought, surprised at how his fingers were trembling slightly as he unlocked the door of his suite.

'Not usually. It's you. You bring out the worst in me,' he groaned huskily, letting her in, throwing the door closed, reaching for her without even turning on the light, their uncontrollable need for each other given full rein now that they were finally alone. 'Oh, *amore*, I've waited so long for this.'

He was tugging off her raincoat, helping her take his from him, their abandoned passion leaving a stream of discarded garments across the dark sitting room and the room beyond.

until they fell mindlessly together onto the luxury of the king-sized bed.

And then there was no more room for words, just a gathering of senses, a different communication, the feel of skin against heated skin, of masculine strength against feminine softness, a moment's sharp pain and then the widening, mind-blowing ecstasies of paradise, a conflagration of desire that consumed them both, carrying them beyond the boundaries of unimagined pleasure until it exploded in a starburst of throbbing sensation, leaving them tumbling, down and down into the sweet, sated aftermath of passion.

'You could be pregnant now,' he said a long time afterwards as she lay in the cradle of his shoulder beneath the sensuous softness of the duvet. His hand was surprisingly arousing over the warm, flat plane of her belly.

'Yes.' She'd thought about it fleetingly beforehand, but she'd been too aroused—as he had been—to do anything about it, despite the conversation they had had that night at his villa.

'Would you mind?' He sounded concerned. But that was just the point. She wouldn't.

Cagily, though, staring up into the darkness, she murmured. 'Wouldn't you?' If he didn't want to tie himself down in any way...

'What do you think?' he breathed.

She didn't have to. She already knew what his feelings were.

'Did you know that Italy has one of the lowest birth rates in the world?' He had digressed from the problem of her possible pregnancy. Or perhaps he didn't consider it a problem, she thought fleetingly—uneasily. 'Not only that— we're actually a declining population. Our numbers are steadily dropping.'

She gave a tremulous little giggle. 'I don't believe it. With all those Latin lovers—' her hand stole provocatively down over his hard, warm hip '—like you?'

He groaned pleasurably, lifting to her more intimate caress. She didn't want to talk about his country's social problems. She wanted him to hold her, to tell her that, whatever happened, everything was going to be all right.

'Perhaps what they're missing is you,' he drawled. 'But you're all mine.' He rolled round so that he was lying on top of her again, taking his weight on his elbows, the lamp he'd reached over to snap on illuminating his strong, dark features.

He smiled when she gasped at his hardening arousal, little knowing of the warmth his possessive statement had spread through her.

'How about it?' he asked, his eyes suddenly sombre beneath the thick fringes of his lashes. 'How about making babies with me?'

Chelsea's face registered shocked surprise. 'For Italy?' She tried to jest, not sure exactly what he was asking of her.

'No, for me and you. As part of us both.' He was kissing her cheek, her temple, the soft, pale honey of her hair.

'Are you saying...?' She paused, her heart beating immeasurably fast. 'Shouldn't you be asking me to...marry you first? Or at least...to live with you?' she uttered tentatively, still unsure.

'That didn't seem to worry you too much just now,' he delivered with a strangely reproving line to his mouth that made her spirits plummet. Hadn't he already told her that night at the villa that he could never offer her what Julian had been offering? 'Would you do that? Simply live with me—*and* have my children?' He sounded rather surprised.

'Yes.'

'And that would be enough?' He was frowning down at her as though he couldn't quite believe it.

It would have to be her heart cried out to him. She only knew that she couldn't live without him, that she would grasp at anything he offered, no matter how flimsy or ill-advised—and on his terms.

'Yes.'

His breath came heavily through distended nostrils. Was he pleased? Relieved? she wondered, starting as he suddenly rasped, 'Well, it wouldn't be enough for me! Of course I want you to marry me first!'

He sounded annoyed that she could even have imagined otherwise. 'As much as I like the idea of...shacking up, is it?...in sin with you, I prefer to bring up my children within the confines of a secure partnership. Not that the exchange of rings between a couple necessarily makes them any more secure—' A deeply personal emotion coloured his voice. 'Gina and Giorgio were an example of that. It's the emotional ties that count.

'But I suppose Dulcie's right. I am old-fashioned in some things. And I've realised I want the woman I love to be my wife in law as well as in her heart. I also have an equally old-fashioned mother, who I think would very probably frown upon my presenting her with grandchildren born outside the accepted bonds of matrimony.'

Chelsea could scarcely believe what she was hearing. 'Are—are you sure?' she breathed, her eyes desperately questioning his as though at any second he might tell her that he was only kidding, that of course he hadn't meant a word of what he'd said.

'I've never been more sure of anything in my life.' Gently he kissed the tip of her small chin. 'What happened to Gina and Giorgio—I let it affect me for too long. I was starting to fester inside. Turning into a bitter, cynical—' He broke off as though he couldn't find quite the right word to describe himself. 'At least where marriage was concerned. But I want and need marriage, Chelsea—and with you. We've both been affected by other people's marriages. It made you want to rush into one, me want to shy away from any suggestion of it, but we'll make ours work—that's a promise.' And then, as though he'd been too premature, he said, 'That's if you want to marry me, of course.'

'Oh, yes!' Chelsea could scarcely contain the joy that seemed to be bubbling through her. And with a teasing lightness she told him, 'I won't force you to live in sin. I love you...' Overcome by her feelings for this man who had seemed so far out of her reach just a few hours ago and who had now confessed his innermost feelings for her, she pressed her lips to his shoulder, inhaling the damp, exciting musk of his skin, and ran her tongue along the dark, velvety flesh, over his chest, against the familiar, dark protrusion of his scar. 'Perhaps,' she said, when she could speak again, 'we should ask Dulcibella to be bridesmaid.'

'You would consider that?' Obviously she had surprised him. 'After what she did to you?'

'Why not?' She lifted her hand to run her fingers down the strong and so dear line of his cheek and jaw. 'If she hadn't said those things we might never have met. And it's partly because of her that I've got you.'

'We've got each other,' he amended with a gentle finger on her nose. 'And that might not have happened if she hadn't let slip what a noble and flawless character I am.' He was laughing, but Chelsea hastened to correct what she knew he still seriously believed.

'I loved you even without that,' she whispered, thinking of all those weeks of agony when she'd prayed for some contact from him. 'All that did was make it worse. I think I knew—all along—in my heart—that you could never have been so merciless as to actually have left Neil...' Her delicate features mirrored the depths of her emotion. 'Perhaps if Dulcibella hadn't accused you of being blind...'

What had Sophia said that day about her granddaughter needing to channel her rebellion into something positive and constructive? Well, hadn't she at last, if only unintentionally, Chelsea thought, by defying Paolo as she had and visiting her? 'Surely we owe her something.'

He chuckled deeply and sensually. 'Perhaps we do,' he agreed. 'But when she threw those remarks at me she only hastened my decision to do what I'd been intending to do all along—to come and court you. Woo you...' His breath trembled through his lungs as he kissed her lightly on her nose, her chin, the scented column of her neck. 'You're very forgiving,' he murmured huskily.

'When things turn out my way I can be,' she responded with a playful little giggle. 'We'll sort her out—together,' she promised softly, caressing the hard velvet warmth of his shoulder. 'We won't let her ruin her life because of that traumatic period in her childhood. We can give her all the understanding she needs.'

'*Carissima . . .*' That one shuddering endearment expressed all the powerful emotion that she could feel emanating from him. 'Chelsea Rossetti.' He made it sound like pure sensuality, like music. 'My wife.'

It sounded good, and she murmured her approval. Then, a little diffidently, she said, 'And you won't force Dad to wear a morning suit?'

'I wouldn't wear one of those things myself,' he assured her laughingly.

'But won't it seem odd,' she said on a mischievous little note, 'if the wife of the man who owns one of the world's leading fashion houses still wears chainstore clothes?'

She was only half-serious, but he smiled and said, 'Not if you promise me never to relinquish that part of you that would probably make you do it. You can wear anything you like.' His hands ran over her nakedness, his eyes appreciating, adoring her. 'But I'd prefer you always to look like this.'

'All the time?' she queried, quaveringly because of what he was doing to her.

His lips moved wryly. 'Most of the time.'

'What about when people are around?' she asked, pretending to take him seriously.

'There won't be anyone else around.' He grimaced. 'Not if I can help it.'

She laughed, loving him. 'You're incorrigible!'

'Incorri— What?'

She laughed again. She loved it when she could outsmart him—which was next to never; already she was beginning to appreciate that. 'It means wonderfully, delightfully *bad . . .*' As she said it she brought her arms above her head in a provocatively submissive arc.

'And you're argumentative,' he said, responding to her invitation with little nipping kisses along her throat.

'I know. Don't you want an argumentative wife?'

'Not if she argues when I am trying to make love to her.'

Excitement throbbed way down in her lower abdomen. 'I thought you just did.'

'That's what I love about you: you don't know when to stop.'

'Do you?' she challenged him, stimulated by this verbal exchange.

'Yes, but I don't intend to.' His hands were arousing her too now.

'Even for meals?'

He let out an impatient sigh. 'Will you shut up?'

'No.' She sucked in her breath at the touch of his gently fondling hands. 'I like antagonising you.'

'Why?'

She sighed, her eyes and her smile sultry. 'You excite me when you're angry.'

'*Mamma mia!* I'm getting a wife who argues with me just because it turns her on?'

Chelsea gave a shy little giggle—shy because now he knew.

His eyes were glittering wickedly as he smiled down at her. 'What can she possibly be imagining I might do to her?'

She wriggled invitingly in response to the dark excitement in his voice, and, stretching her arms further above her, in total submission to it, murmured, 'Do anything you like with her, Paolo.'

He laughed meaningfully under his breath. Then, bending his dark head, silencing her with his kiss, he proceeded to do just that.

IRON LACE
Emilie Richards

Behind the iron lace gates of wealthy New
Orleans, and beneath the veneer of her society
name, lingers truths that Aurore Gerritsen has
hidden for a lifetime—truths that threaten to
change forever the lives of her unsuspecting
family. Now, as Aurore faces her own mortality,
she needs to reveal the secrets that have haunted
her for so many years.

Aurore seeks out Phillip Benedict to disclose
her story. Though intrigued by the proposal,
Phillip wonders why the matriarch of a
prominent white family would choose to tell her
story to an outspoken black journalist.

Finally, Phillip agrees, knowing that he's been
handed the most explosive story of his life.
But nothing prepares him for the far-reaching
impact of Aurore's shocking revelations.

*"Deeply moving, Iron Lace is a break-your-
heart love story."*
> Karen Harper, author of *Dark Road Home*

*"...vividly drawn characters...brilliantly
complex work."*
> Affaire de Coeur

MILLS & BOON®

Next Month's Romances

♡

Each month you can choose from a wide variety of romance with Mills & Boon. Below are the new titles to look out for next month in our two new series Presents and Enchanted.

Presents™

THEIR WEDDING DAY	Emma Darcy
THE FINAL PROPOSAL	Robyn Donald
HIS BABY!	Sharon Kendrick
MARRIED FOR REAL	Lindsay Armstrong
MISTLETOE MAN	Kathleen O'Brien
BAD INFLUENCE	Susanne McCarthy
TORN BY DESIRE	Natalie Fox
POWERFUL PERSUASION	Margaret Mayo

Enchanted™

THE VICAR'S DAUGHTER	Betty Neels
BECAUSE OF THE BABY	Debbie Macomber
UNEXPECTED ENGAGEMENT	Jessica Steele
BORROWED WIFE	Patricia Wilson
ANGEL BRIDE	Barbara McMahon
A WIFE FOR CHRISTMAS	Pamela Bauer & Judy Kaye
ALL SHE WANTS FOR CHRISTMAS	Liz Fielding
TROUBLE IN PARADISE	Grace Green

Available from WH Smith, John Menzies, Volume One, Forbuoys, Martins, Woolworths, Tesco, Asda, Safeway and other paperback stockists.

SINGLE LETTER SWITCH

A year's supply of Mills & Boon Presents™ novels— absolutely FREE!

Would you like to win a year's supply of passionate compelling and provocative romances? Well, you can and the're free! Simply complete the grid below and send it to us by 31st May 1997. The first five correct entries picked after the closing date will win a year's supply of Mills & Boon Presents™ novels (six books every month—worth over £150). What could be easier?

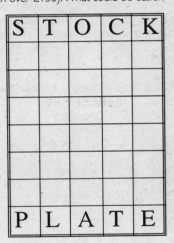

S	T	O	C	K
P	L	A	T	E

Clues:

A   To pile up
B   To ease off or a reduction
C   A dark colour
D   Empty or missing
E   A piece of wood
F   Common abbreviation for an aircraft

Please turn over for details of how to enter ☞

How to enter...

There are two five letter words provided in the grid overleaf. The first one being STOCK the other PLATE. All you have to do is write down the words that are missing by changing just one letter at a time to form a new word and eventually change the word STOCK into PLATE. You only have eight chances but we have supplied you with clues as to what each one is. Good Luck!

When you have completed the grid don't forget to fill in your name and address in the space provided below and pop this page into an envelope (you don't even need a stamp) and post it today. Hurry—competition ends 31st May 1997.

Mills & Boon® Single Letter Switch
FREEPOST
Croydon
Surrey
CR9 3WZ

Are you a Reader Service Subscriber?   Yes ☐   No ☐

Ms/Mrs/Miss/Mr _____

Address _____

_____

_____ Postcode _____

One application per household.

You may be mailed with other offers from other reputable companies as a result of this application. If you would prefer not to receive such offers, please tick box.   ☐

C6K